THE
ILLUSTRATED ENCYCLOPAEDIA
OF ANIMAL LIFE

THE ANIMAL KINGDOM

The strange and wonderful ways of mammals, birds, reptiles, fishes and insects. A new and authentic natural history of the wild life of the world

VOLUME 1

FREDERICK DRIMMER, M.A.
EDITOR-IN-CHIEF

GEORGE G. GOODWIN
*Associate Curator of Mammals,
The American Museum of Natural
History*

CHARLES M. BOGERT
*Curator of Amphibians and Reptiles,
The American Museum of Natural
History*

**DEAN AMADON
E. THOMAS GILLIARD**
*Associate Curators of Birds,
The American Museum of Natural History*

CHRISTOPHER W. COATES *Curator*
JAMES W. ATZ *Assistant Curator*
*Aquarium of The New York Zoological
Society*

JOHN C. PALLISTER
Research Associate, Insects, The American Museum of Natural History

ODHAMS BOOKS LONDON

About This Work

The Illustrated Encyclopaedia of Animal Life is an epochal work in the field of natural history. It has been more than four years in preparation, being written by seven eminent naturalists on the staffs of the American Museum of Natural History and the New York Zoological Society, and by an eighth equally eminent authority, Dorothy Edwards Shuttlesworth. It comprises over two thousand eight hundred and seventy pages and eight hundred thousand words of authentic and interesting information about the wild life of the world. It includes in its entirety the text of the famous multi-volume library, *The Animal Kingdom*, plus one hundred and seventy thousand added words and over thirty times the number of full colour plates! It is far and away the most complete and authoritative up-to-date natural history in the English language.

The Illustrated Encyclopaedia of Animal Life will supply you with the knowledge you need if you are to understand the animals that share the world in which you live. Based on the most recent research and investigation, this great work explains simply and colourfully the intimate lives of wild animals, both common and exotic, of all lands—not only the mammals, but the birds, amphibians, reptiles, fishes, insects and other invertebrates. The writers tell you how you can recognize each important animal, where it lives, its habits, courtship, family life, how it raises its young, how it combats enemies and gets its food, and give a wealth of other fascinating information—in short, the animal's natural history.

ANIMALS ALIVE

This is a library of animals alive. The distinguished authors, although outstanding scientists, are no mere dry-as-dust museum specialists. They have a deep love of animals and have tracked and observed them in the remote fastnesses of the earth.

In these pages they share many a thrilling adventure with you, many a startling encounter they have had in the wild—with giant brown bears and the wolves of the Arctic tundra, with the lions of the African veldt, the poisonous reptiles of the American deserts and woodland, the exotic birds of the rain forests of New Guinea, the strange insects of the jungles of South America. You will read of hairbreadth escapes, and the curious ways of primitive peoples in the native lands of these animals.

A LIBRARY OF MARVELS

This is a library of marvels as well. Animals have a way of not living up to our preconceived notions, yet what they will do often exceeds our most fantastic expectations. Thus the authors tell you about fishes that build nests in the water or hop about on land, about desert rodents that never drink water and will refuse it when offered, about ants that keep herds of insect "cows", salamanders that have elaborate courtship rites, young elephants that make their own playthings, bats that go fishing, whales that commit suicide, birds that cannot fly but can run faster than most other animals.

Nature teems with such oddities, and since they are of considerable scientific and popular interest, the authors describe them at length.

WHAT ANIMALS MEAN TO MAN

This is also an illustrated encyclopaedia about what animals mean to man. The story of how wild creatures are hunted and trapped or tamed is spread through these pages.

You will read here how the Japanese rear silkworms, how the Indians tame the elephant, and how South American natives hunt the capybara, the biggest rodent on earth, along the Orinoco and the Amazon. You will learn how the whale is fished today by modern fleets in the icy waters of the Antarctic, and the uses to which ambergris, whale oil, whale meat, and whalebone are put. Few stories are more tragic than those told here about the large-scale slaughter of fur seals, ostriches, birds of paradise, bison, Colobus monkeys, and other animals, which once brought these creatures close to extinction.

Bears and seals as entertainers—the comparative reliability of lions and tigers as circus performers—the humble origins of some furs with glamorous names—the ancestry of our domestic cats, canaries, and other creatures—these are merely a few of the fascinating subjects touched on, in which man and the animals are linked.

The authors also take you on diverting excursions into the romantic realm of folklore, tell you of the odd beliefs people have about animals around the globe, and explain the origin of many legendary beasts such as the unicorn and the sea serpent.

A WORK OF SCIENTIFIC INFORMATION

Although those aspects of animal life that are of most interest to the general reader have been stressed in this wild-life library, and technical jargon has been avoided, this work is thoroughly scientific in approach and content. You will find highly accurate and lucid explanations of how such mammals as the weasel change colours with the seasons, how the heat-detecting mechanism of reptiles works, how birds can fly, how fishes breathe, and countless other important facts.

The wonderful story of the development of the animals is related simply and clearly, and frequent glimpses are afforded of the rich animal life of the past— of odd or spectacular creatures like the dinosaur and the four-toed horse that became extinct ages ago, as well as those that, like the dodo and the passenger pigeon, vanished within historic time. The common and zoological names of the

various animals are given—approximately eight thousand are listed in the Complete
Ready Reference Index at the end of this work—and their position in the scheme
of living things is explained.

EIGHT EMINENT AUTHORS

To give *The Illustrated Encyclopaedia of Animal Life* unimpeachable authority
the task of producing this monumental work was entrusted to eight leading
authorities on animal life.

Section I—Mammals of the Air, Land, and Waters of the World—was written
by George G. Goodwin, Associate Curator of the Department of Mammals of
the American Museum of Natural History. Dr. Goodwin has studied mammals in
their native habitat all over the world: his explorations have taken him to Siberia,
Turkistan, Persia, Syria, Egypt, Kenya, Tanganyika, the West Indies, the Arctic,
and many other remote places. He has collected forty-five hundred specimens for
the Museum, and named sixty mammals new to science. He is the author of
numerous articles and seventy popular and scientific publications, including
Mammals of Honduras, Mammals of Costa Rica, Mammals of Connecticut, etc.

Although the mammals are not the most numerous of the animals, more interest
attaches to them than to other forms of wild life and so Section I is the longest in
this entire library; in point of fact it is the most up-to-date and comprehensive
popular work on mammals of the world in the English language.

Section II—Birds of the World—is the work of two outstanding bird experts,
Dean Amadon and E. Thomas Gilliard, Associate Curators of the Department of
Birds of the American Museum of Natural History. They have devoted many
years to the study of birds in North and South America, Australia, New Guinea,
the Hawaiian Islands and the Philippines. Dr. Amadon and Mr. Gilliard are the
authors of articles that have appeared in many leading scientific and popular
periodicals.

Section III—Amphibians and Reptiles of the World—was written by Charles M.
Bogert, Chairman and Curator of the Department of Amphibians and Reptiles
at the American Museum of Natural History. A distinguished explorer and scientist,
Mr. Bogert has made many notable scientific contributions concerning the reptiles
and amphibians of the United States, Mexico, Central America, New Guinea, and
Africa. He has taught biology and zoology at the University of California.

Section IV—Fishes of the World—comes from the pens of Christopher W.
Coates, Curator, and James W. Atz, Assistant Curator, of the New York Aquarium
of the New York Zoological Society. Mr. Coates is the leading public aquarist in
the United States, and one of the leaders in the world. For his use of aquatic
animals in medical research he has won two awards for Advancement of Medical
Science. Both Mr. Coates and Mr. Atz are the authors of numerous scientific and
popular writings in their field.

Section V—Insects and Other Invertebrates—is by John C. Pallister, Research
Associate, Department of Insects and Spiders, at the American Museum of Natural
History; he was formerly in charge of the Entomological Department of the Cleve-
land Museum of Natural History. An explorer, scientist, and lecturer of many

years' experience, Mr. Pallister has studied and collected insects and other invertebrates in the United States, Canada, Mexico, Guatemala, British Honduras,
Panama, Brazil, Peru, and on islands in the Pacific.

"Exploring Nature with Your Child" is the overall title of special features, on
green paper, added to each of the 16 volumes. These features were selected by
the famous Dorothy Edwards Shuttlesworth who founded the highly successful
Junior Natural History Magazine and edited it for 19 years. Dr. C. L. Duddington,
M.A., Ph.D., F.L.S.; John Lewis, B.Sc., F.L.S., A.K.C.; and Walter Shepherd,
a member of the Royal Institution and author of *The Countryside Round the
Year*; *A New Survey of Science*; *The Living Landscape of Britain*, etc.; have
contributed to the special features concerning wild life in Britain.

AN IMPRESSIVE GALLERY OF WILD-LIFE PICTURES

Over 570 extraordinary full-colour photographs, plus 134 in black and white,
were assembled from expert colour photographers all over the world. In addition,
another 550 accurate drawings of animals in their natural surroundings were
especially prepared for this library by famous wild-life artists, in most cases working
directly with the authors.

Many other persons have given freely of their time and thought to help make
The Illustrated Encyclopaedia of Animal Life the classic work in its field. In particular, the publishers wish to acknowledge a debt of gratitude to Dr. Roy Chapman
Andrews, President Emeritus of the American Museum of Natural History, for his
generous encouragement during the initial stages. Dr. George G. Goodwin gave
invaluable advice and guidance as the book grew, and so, too, did the other authors.

In its domain, this great work has no equal. We may still profitably follow the
counsel of the Bible: "Go to the ant, thou sluggard; consider her ways, and be
wise." There is no substitute for going out and seeing the animals at first hand,
and it is hoped that the present work will encourage the reader to do so. But for a
general understanding of the animals, however, we no longer need to travel afield,
nor, indeed, to look into a multitude of books on the different classes of animal life.
The Illustrated Encyclopaedia of Animal Life now tells us, clearly and expertly,
within the scope of a single comprehensive natural history, the things we want to
know about the strange and wonderful ways of them all—the mammals, birds,
amphibians, reptiles, fishes, insects and other invertebrates of the entire world.

FREDERICK DRIMMER
Editor-in-Chief

Contents

Section 1: Mammals of the Air, Land, and Waters of the World

By George G. Goodwin

[1-A]

Bull moose wage terrific battles sometimes to determine the leader of the herd and often, during the mating season, for possession of the cows, doing considerable damage not only to each other but to the surrounding landscape. Largest member of the deer family, a full-grown bull stands almost six feet at the shoulder and weighs up to 1400 pounds. His antlers may spread more than 70 inches.
See page 739

The largest of the antelopes, the eland got its name from early Dutch
settlers in Africa—the only place it is to be found. Although the
word means "elk" the eland is quite different from the elk and even
from other antelopes. The blue-grey colour is typical of old bulls.
See page 793

[1-B]

Section II: Birds of the World

By Dean Amadon
and E. Thomas Gilliard

Section III: Amphibians and Reptiles of the World

By Charles M. Bogert

AMPHIBIANS, PIONEERS ON LAND

1191
Vol. 10

Where the amphibians came from — where the amphibians live - the three groups of amphibians.

[1-E]

The camera "stopped" this charging rhinoceros, but the blurred background gives some idea of the speed with which these cumbersome creatures can move. The "horns" are hard cones of curiously matted hair, highly prized in some areas as a love-potion.

See page 670

A sockeye salmon clears a waterfall on the way upstream to the spawning area. Salmon will travel 2000 miles, overcoming all sorts of obstacles, to return to the particular freshwater area where they were hatched—only to lay their eggs and die. The few who never leave the area also die after spawning, so it is not the rigours of the journey which cause their death. *See page 1448*

[1-G]

One hazard the migrating salmon encounter is the Alaska brown bear. The bears wade in the rapids and below waterfalls, scooping out the fish with a quick sweep of their strong claws. If the catch is good, the bears will eat only the soft insides, and the expectant gulls will be well rewarded. See page 472

At least 44 different popular names have been recorded for the largemouth black bass. Call it what you will, this foot-long specimen is very much at home in weedy, sluggish water. Because of its great adaptability to warm still water, the largemouth is used extensively in pond culture and has been introduced into such far-away places as South Africa and Hawaii. *See page 1532*

Section IV: Fishes of the World

By Christopher W. Coates
and James W. Atz

Section V: Insects and other Invertebrates

By John C. Pallister

[1-C]

A clumsy, ungainly creature on land and only a little better in the water, the walrus can yet negotiate the rocky surf without difficulty. Almost hairless, the walrus depends upon a heavy layer of blubber beneath its tough, thick hide for protection against the Arctic cold.
See page 608

[1-D]

The camel family had its start not in Africa but in North America—
40,000,000 years ago. Today the only remaining members of the
group are the South American llamas and the familiar "ship of the
desert". In spite of their reputation for bad temper, obstinacy and
true grudge carrying, when treated with kindness and understanding
camels are gentle and co-operative. *See page 698*

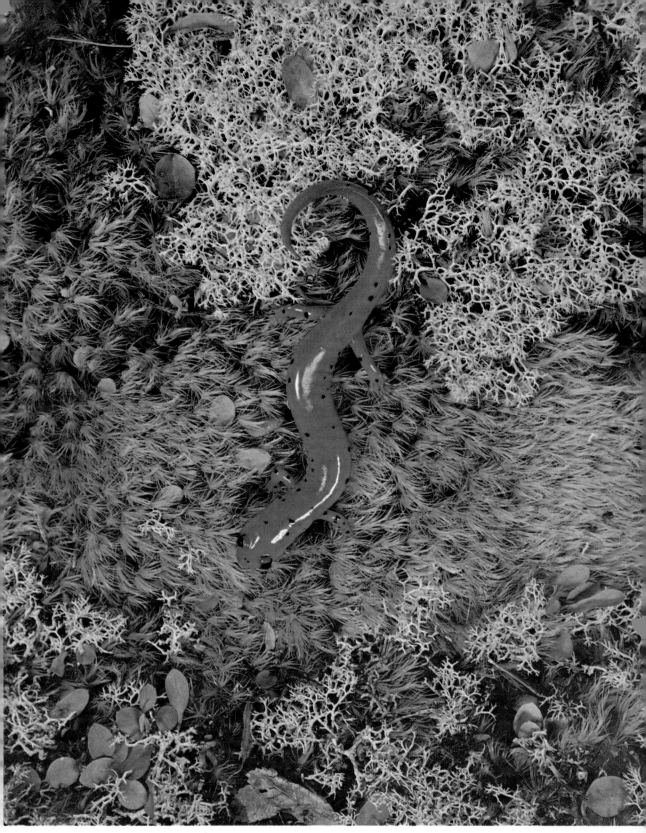

[1-I]

An eastern mud salamander rests on a bed of moss and lichens.
Amphibians with tails, salamanders have the moist skin typical of
the group. While some varieties breathe through the skin, others
have lungs and still others have gills like fish. They also vary greatly
in size—from two inches to five feet in length.   *See page 1194*

Australia's thorny, or mountain, devil is the counterpart of the American horned lizard ("toad"). The horns and enlarged scales not only obscure the body outline, making the animal more difficult to see, but also serve rather effectively as weapons of defence.

See page 1307

PAGE

Special Features on Green Paper

Exploring Nature with Your Child

Section 1

MAMMALS OF THE AIR, LAND, AND WATERS OF THE WORLD

——

GEORGE G. GOODWIN

Understanding the Mammals

MANY and wonderful are the differences we find among the mammals that live in the world today. They vary in size from the tiny shrew that weighs only a fraction of an ounce to the gigantic whale that weighs a hundred tons. They vary in habit from the timid little squirrel that feeds on acorns to the amiable dolphin that plucks fishes from the deep, and the ferocious big cats that sometimes prey even on man. Their diversity seems almost infinite, and their ways, whether formed by instinct or learning, are nothing short of amazing.

From the largest to the smallest, there is exquisite beauty and grandeur of form in nearly every type of animal; we see grace and rhythm in practically every motion. Each animal comes close to perfection in its own manner. True, none has quite learned to think and talk as we can do, but they have developed enough mental power for their own needs. Not only can some animals give voice to their feelings of love, friendship, fear, hate, and rage, but many have a system of code signals which they use to communicate with one another.

Outside man's domain, the mammals have made themselves at home practically everywhere. Looking at some of the hard, unfriendly places where they have settled, we are often compelled to marvel that they could survive there at all. We discover mammals living under conditions ranging from intense cold to tropical heat, from the rarefied air of snow-capped peaks to the depths of the ocean. On fields of floating ice and in the heart of the arid, burning desert, mammals have made their dwelling places.

Some mammals, such as the bats, have taken to the air. Others, like the squirrels and monkeys, have entered the forests and climbed the trees. The whales and seals have left the land and gone to sea. Animals

3

have covered the face of the earth; some, such as the gopher and mole, have burrowed underground. Wherever there was living space for them, the mammals have moved in.

In all these different kinds of places, we find the mammals superbly equipped to meet Nature's challenge. To withstand the rigours of a cold climate, many are clad in thick, woolly fur. Others that spend much of their time swimming in streams and lakes have oily hair that sheds water. The covering of the mammals may range from the super-fine fur of the chinchilla to the barbed quills of the porcupine or to the horny shell of the armadillo.

WHY WE CALL THEM MAMMALS

An outer covering of hair is the peculiar property of the mammals. Not every mammal possesses one—a few, like the whale, are practically hairless. On the other hand, we do find hair on the bodies of most mammals. This is in sharp contrast to other classes of animal life. The birds, fishes, and reptiles are not protected by such a growth.

Still, this covering is only one of the typical features of the mammals. Strictly speaking, we consider everything that lives and is not a plant to be an animal—just what things make us call this group of animals "mammals" and nothing else? The name "mammal" comes from the Latin word *mamma*, meaning "breast". The mammals have glands that produce milk which they use to feed their young. Except for a few primitive mammals, which lay eggs, all bear their babies alive, and even the egg-layers suckle their young. It is in these characteristics that we find the sharpest differences between the mammals and other animals.

Mammals, of course, possess backbones and breathe air. Even a whale will drown if it cannot surface regularly to draw life-giving oxygen into its lungs. Like the birds, but like no other animals, the mammals have a four-chambered heart and a complete double system of circula-tion—on one side impure blood is carried to the lungs, where the poisonous gases escape; on the other side, after being refreshed with oxygen, the blood is piped back to the rest of the body.

Unlike the fishes and the reptiles—but again like the birds—mammals are warm-blooded. To maintain their body temperature, they rely not only on their hairy covering, but on still another mechanism other animals do not have: the sweat glands.

We never find more than two pairs of limbs on a mammal. Some mammals, like the kangaroo, have hind legs that represent an extreme in development. At the opposite end of the picture is the whale, which has lost its hind limbs altogether and acquired flukes to help it move about in the water.

Every mammal has front limbs—even the bats, which have developed them into wings for flight. In the whale they have become flippers. Look at the skeleton of a whale the next time you visit a museum and you will see the bones—vaguely reminiscent of those in the human hand—that gave the flippers support when the huge creature was alive.

The driving power of most mammals is centred in their hind limbs. All fast runners have longer tips on their toes to increase their speed, and they possess cushioned pads for support. Some, like the sheep, deer and horses, have their toes encased in hoofs, and the middle toe or toes take over the function of the foot, at the expense of the other toes.

KEEN SENSES

As a rule, the senses of sight, taste, smell, hearing, and touch are well developed in the mammals. What an animal lacks in one sense, it frequently makes up in another. The mole, for example, is almost completely blind, but it has a highly sensitive nose and tail to guide it around in the darkness.

Some animals also tend to specialize in the development of one sense organ though not at the expense of another. The monkeys and their relatives, spending their lives in the trees, where vision is at a premium, often have unusually large eyes. In the deserts, where the sun is dazzling and where there is little opportunity to find cover, we often observe that the animals possess big ears, helping them to detect danger while it is still far off.

Most mammals live in a dull, grey world. Only a few—the apes, for example—have colour vision. Others—usually animals that are active at night, like the cats—are famous because their eyes glow in the dark. The eyes, however, do not generate any light themselves; they merely catch up and reflect whatever light is present in the gloom. Behind this remarkable power lies an interesting fact. The inner wall of the eye is coated with a substance called "guanin". This has a metallic lustre of silver or gold and brightens dimly lit images on the retina of the animal's eye so that it can see them better.

The sense of touch is far more vital to an animal than you might suppose. Almost every motion is closely connected with the sense of touch. Nerve fibres end in tiny raised points on the skin which are known as touch spots. Except on the soles of the feet, a touch spot usually has a hair on it. The hairs themselves are not sensitive, but they act as levers to press the touch spots. Animals are guided in running or walking by this sense of touch. The long hairs or whiskers on the nose of the cat are connected with touch spots and supplement sight in dim light.

CAMOUFLAGED BY NATURE

The sharpest sense of animals is sight. It is the swiftest, too: seeing takes place with the speed of light. Falcons, hawks, and the fastest beasts of prey hunt by sight. A tiger may track a goat by scent, but the final leap is guided by sight.

Still, many animals possess a means of defeating this exceedingly sharp sense. Protective coloration can create an optical illusion that will deceive the keenest observer. How inconspicuous an animal may be depends on how well it blends in with its surroundings. Natural camouflage not only enables an animal to escape detection by its enemies; it causes the flesh-eater to be less avoided by the animals it preys on.

GAY COATS ARE CAMOUFLAGE, TOO

Some animals are gaudily coloured, but are camouflaged none the less. The chequered sunfleck and leaf-shadow pattern of the leopard, ocelot, jaguar, and giraffe, though contrasting and conspicuous when you view it in a zoological garden, fades to obscurity in the bush. In Kenya the author saw a leopard take its stand in a bright sunlit opening against a background of bush; but a white hunter, a sports-man, and his gunbearer could not see the animal at seventy-five feet although they gazed at the exact spot where it stood for fully fifteen minutes.

It might seem that the extraordinary, brilliant, clear-cut black-and-white-striped coat of a zebra would make it a marked animal that could not escape detection. Nor does it—on the open veldt. But the zebra must go regularly to some pool to drink, and here, where lions are poised to pounce, the stripes become an asset. At the water's edge, silhouetted against tall, light-coloured reeds and a shadowy background, the showy zebra pattern fades to a beneficial obscurity. In the same way the vertical stripes of a tiger's coat bear a graceful resemblance to the bushy and grassy thickets of its hunting-ground.

CAMOUFLAGE LIGHT AND DARK

Beasts of the open plains—such as lions, kangaroos, hares and the like —are noted for their lack of markings, but they still illustrate the fundamental principle of animal camouflage. The under-parts of these animals are usually white, or lighter than the colour of the back. The brightest light comes from above and lightens the back, but throws the under-parts in shadow, so that both upper and lower parts look alike; the outline of the animal is thus flattened and blotted out in certain lights if the animal is motionless.

Light and dark shades in the covering of an animal are often graduated so that it is less conspicuous when viewed either from above or from below, depending on which aspect it is most often seen from. Many animals that live close to the soil are ground-coloured. A grey squirrel has an over-all covering of white-tipped hairs that make it hard to see in the trees, against the sky.

CHANGING WITH THE SEASONS

The camouflage pattern of an animal's coat is not always fixed. In regions where seasons bring drastic changes in temperature and in the colour of the surroundings, some animals not only vary the thickness of their coat but change its colour as a concealing factor. The ermine and varying hare, for example, have brown fur in summer, which makes it difficult to see them on the forest floor; in winter they are equally inconspicuous against a snow-covered background, for now their coats have been changed to white.

These temporary white winter coats of northern animals should not be confused with albinism. Albinism is a sign of weakness, often accompanied by pink eyes and poor eyesight, whereas the change in the ermine and the varying hare is a normal, regular happening.

MILLS THAT GRIND AND CUT

Almost anything that can be eaten serves as food for some kind of animal, and each creature is specialized more or less to one type of diet. The cattle are grass-eaters, the deer are leaf-eaters, the beavers eat the bark of trees. The wild cats live mainly on flesh; there are bats that actually drain the nectar of flowers; some animals depend on a diet of insects or shellfish, or fruits, nuts, and seeds.

To feed on these diets, hard or soft, mammals often have special kinds of teeth. In general, a mammal's teeth are not all the same, as they are in the lower animals with backbones. In one mammal, like the tiger, we find large canine teeth that seize and rend the flesh of their prey, and cheek teeth adapted for biting; some have heavy molars that help in grinding, and other types of teeth.

The lower animals, like the shark, will grow a new tooth to take the place of an old one, and can go on doing this indefinitely. Not so the mammals—they have only two sets of teeth: the "milk teeth" and the "permanent teeth". They seldom have more than forty-four teeth, generally fewer. The monkeys of the Old World, for example, have thirty-two, the same number as man.

So far as teeth go, most of us have reason to envy the mammals; theirs will last them through life. Some mammals, like the beaver and other rodents—animals that gnaw their food—have long front teeth whose growth never ceases. The teeth of the horse and many other animals that grind their food continue to grow until late in life.

Animals that feed on tough, rough vegetation have sturdier teeth than those that eat soft, pulpy food. Insect-eaters like the ant-eater and the pangolin have no teeth whatever—instead, they have a long, extendible tongue to lick up their victims, which they swallow whole. Many whales are toothless, too; their mouths are provided with baleen, an efficient strainer that permits them to separate from the water the minute sea life with which they maintain their huge bodies.

Teeth provide valuable clues to the naturalist who is trying to identify an animal. They are often the one feature by which we can definitely recognize a species. It does not matter that the animal's bones may have been scattered or turned to dust a hundred, a thousand, or even a million years ago. If we find the teeth, they reveal the nature of the animal to us, for each species has its own typical set.

HOW ANIMALS MOVE ABOUT

All members of the animal kingdom live and move. We associate life with motion, and the panorama of life interests us only because it changes and moves. Indeed, it would almost appear that man's emotional stability is governed by motion. Inactivity brings loneliness and despair, while motion means life and brings hope. To no small degree, living things are pleasing to have around because they move. The stillness of death appears unnatural to us and causes us distress.

Motion is not confined to the animal kingdom—modern science has shown us that all matter is in motion. The sea and the air are at their grandest during a storm. The lightning-flash followed by the growl of thunder reminds us that all is in action. Nature gives us no example of absolute rest. In time even the rocks grow old and crumble into dust.

Man, by observing Nature, has been able to learn many valuable lessons. Seeing that birds and insects could fly, he eventually learned to fly himself. If he had never witnessed these models in the air, he might very likely have assumed that flight was impossible—had he thought about it at all.

The forces employed in walking, swimming, and flying are basically the same. It is largely because the elements in which the animals travel are different that their way of getting about varies. Land is more solid and firmer than water, and water has a greater density than air.

ANIMALS OF LAND, WATER, AND AIR

Whatever the element may be—land, water, or air—each has its advantages and disadvantages. On dry land a horse must not only support its own weight but also generate the power necessary to drive itself along. On the other hand, the body of a whale is supported by the buoyancy of the sea; all its exertions can be centred on moving itself, but it must make a greater effort to force its way through water than would be the case in air. Some birds like the albatross can soar for an hour without flapping a wing; but such a bird must have huge wing muscles to hold it suspended in the air.

An animal's power to move is centred in its limbs or other extremities. The wings of a bird support and carry it through the air. The tail of the fishes and the flukes of a whale are propellers that push these animals through the water—but its chief driving force here consists of the undulations of the body itself. Land mammals, of course, travel by means of their legs.

WONDERFUL FEET AND LEGS

Every living thing impresses us as a miracle of adaptation, once we look at it closely. Take the lowly housefly, for example. It has, on the ends of its feet, suction discs that enable it to stay on a ceiling and walk upside down. The feet of the mammals are no less interesting. Animals that climb rocky mountain slopes have rubber-like pads on their feet as a safety device. The chamois, one of Nature's ablest mountaineers, is shod with a pliable, horny hoof encasing a rubbery sole— a combination that will not only hold on slippery rocks but acts as a shock-absorber as well. A camel that travels over the shifting sands would quickly tire were its feet not equipped with a broad pad that spreads when it is pressed on the ground, giving added support.

With the exception of leaping animals, most land-bound mammals move diagonally forward—the right front leg and the left hind leg move forward together, alternating with the left front leg and hind right leg. This is also true of ourselves. As we put our right leg forward, our left arm moves with it; a similar action of our left foot and right arm follows. With this diagonal movement of the limbs the body twists and weaves forward with an even continuity of movement.

ANIMALS THAT PACE

There is no doubt that this pendulum motion of the limbs and body is the most efficient method for travel on land, yet not all four-footed animals progress in this manner. A very few amble or pace. In these the fore and hind limbs on one side move forward at the same time, first on one side then on the other. Pacing is hereditary and has been handed down among these creatures for ages.

Animals that pace have their body slung high on their legs but they are not restricted to any particular kind of dwelling place. The camel is the most popular example of a pacer, but the llama, alpaca, and their wild camel-like relatives of the Andes are also pacers. The giraffe of

[1-K]

The red sided garter snake belongs to the most widely distributed and most frequently encountered snake family in the United States. Fortunately, they are not poisonous. While most common garter snakes are grey with ill-defined stripes, colour and pattern may vary considerably, not only in different parts of the country but within a relatively small area. *See page 1339*

Gulls are the most graceful of all flying birds and, with their webbed feet, are equally at home on the water. They survive fierce storms at sea, resting on the waves, and flourish in the severest extremes of climate. Although avid scavengers, the gulls are exceptionally clean birds. *See page 1024*

UNGAINLY ON LAND BUT A CHAMPION IN THE WATER

Long ages ago, the ancestors of the fur seal had legs like other land mammals, but these limbs developed into flippers when the animals took to the water. Ungainly on land, the fur seal is exceedingly graceful and swift when it swims. The animal shown here is a young male. *See page 601.*

South African Railways

THE SWIFTEST OF ALL LAND MAMMALS STALKS ITS PREY

The cheetah, a big cat of Asia and Africa, can cover a distance of one hundred yards in four and one-half seconds, but it cannot keep up this pace for long. In India for hundreds of years tame cheetahs have been used to bring down game. *See page 595.*

THE FEROCIOUS BOBCAT NEED FEAR FEW ENEMIES

A skilful climber and a speedy runner, the bobcat can generally protect itself against most natural enemies. It hunts mainly by night, taking an extensive toll of rabbits, squirrels, mice, other small game. *See page 565.*

Paul A. Moore — Tenn. Conservation Dept.

the African veldt is a pacer, as is the okapi of the Congo forests. The hyena paces; some horses inherit a like tendency to pace. This is not artificial, although it is developed by trainers.

THEIR TAILS HELP THEM TRAVEL

The tail plays an important part in helping many animals to move about. Squirrels have need of a bushy tail to maintain their balance in the treetops and to guide their descent in their flying leaps. Many jumping animals have a long tail and use it as a rudder when sailing through the air. The great kangaroo makes long leaps, sometimes covering about forty feet, and is given an extra boost by its powerful tail. Passing from the great to the small, we find that all the jumping mice have exceptionally long tails to steer them through the air. Most monkeys have a long tail as a balancing organ; the South American monkey can often use it as a fifth hand.

Of course many mammals with only the scantiest trace of a tail do very nicely all the same. The African antelope, the impala, covers up to thirty-five feet in a jump without any assistance from its short tail. A jack rabbit has been known to clear a fence seven feet high; as many of us know, the little powder puff on the rear end of a rabbit is used as a signal and for nothing else.

SPEED RECORDS IN THE ANIMAL KINGDOM

Fishes are built for easy travel through the water. While a fish's principal power comes from the manipulation or weaving motion of the body, it possesses auxiliary motors for jet propulsion. In a sudden burst of speed a fish ejects a fast stream of water through its gills. It is generally accepted that the fastest living creature in the water is the sailfish, with a possible or estimated maximum speed of 68 miles per hour. The swordfish and the marlin are also fast travellers—they are reported as capable of speeds up to 60 miles per hour. Dolphins are the fastest marine mammals with a motor power that can drive them up to 37 miles per hour.

BIRDS ARE FASTEST

The record speed for any animal is held by a bird—the frigate bird has a flying speed of over 100 miles per hour and has been credited with a hard-to-believe record of over twice this speed. The swifts are among the fastest of all birds, but it is doubtful if the spine-tailed swift ever attained 219 miles per hour, as recorded. The peregrine falcon can speed up its flight to around 100 miles per hour, not taking into account power dives or aid from favourable winds.

Geese, which have been timed by aircraft instruments, can travel at 60 miles per hour, and they hold the altitude record of 29,000 feet, which is nearly $5\frac{1}{2}$ miles. However, except during migration, birds usually fly at an altitude below 2,000 feet.

MAMMALS BUILT FOR SPEED

When we come to the mammals, the record, although good, cannot rival that of the birds. The fastest four-footed animal on land is the cheetah, with a stop-watch record of 70 miles per hour. It probably has an even greater maximum speed.

The Mongolian antelope and the American pronghorn can keep ahead of an automobile with the speedometer registering 60. The fastest speed ever recorded for a racehorse is 48 miles per hour. Some hares come close to this—they can travel at a speed of 45 miles per hour, which is about the same as the top speed for a big kangaroo.

In general, four legs are better than two; the top speed at which a man can run is only just over 22 miles per hour for 100 yards, while a greyhound can streak along at 40 miles and still be left behind by a hare. The slowest mammal is the sloth, which on the ground cannot reach a pace higher than five-tenths of a mile per hour.

In speed, the mammals have gone far beyond their reptile forebears. A man can easily escape from most snakes found in the United States and Europe. The African mamba, which grows to a length of 12 feet, is one of the fastest snakes on earth, with an estimated speed of 10 miles an hour. It is also one of the most dangerous, as it attacks without provocation and takes the offensive when man or beast enters its home territory.

SMALL BUT SWIFT

The smallest members of the animal kingdom are by no means the slowest. In the insect world there are dragonflies that can travel at 55 miles per hour; a worker honeybee 15, a queen 20, and a drone 25 miles per hour. The last two have 330 wingbeats to the second!

ANIMALS OF THE NIGHT AND DAY

For most mammals, the bright sunlight hours around midday and the darkest hours of the night are a time for resting and sleeping. Some, like the tree squirrels and their kind, may be abroad during the warm part of the day, but most prefer to stay in their nests and dens, or hide in the underbrush.

It is when the shadows begin to lengthen that all nature really comes to life, and the woods and countryside hum with activity. In the twilight, most mammals eat their big meal of the day. Grazing and browsing animals, like the hippopotamus and the antelope, come out of their places of concealment and feed steadily in the cool of the evening and well on into the night. On the wing at sunset, the bats have eaten their fill of fruit and insects and returned to their roosts before midnight; they may go out hunting again in the wee hours of the morning.

There are a few strictly night prowlers, like the wolves, tigers, and other flesh-eaters, that will continue their search for prey all night if their hunger has not been appeased. Many rodents are not only active by night, but all through the day, too. They must eat constantly, for they are energetic little creatures and their bodies quickly burn up all the food they can provide themselves with. By and large, though, most animals are active at dusk.

LIVING BY INSTINCT

An animal is born with an inherited sense that it obeys without question. It comes into the world with the ability to act and protect itself according to its immediate needs—without instruction or learning gained from experience. This is what we mean by animal instinct.

Instinct is generous and motherly; it gathers all life under its protecting shelter. It covers a wide field of animal behaviour, from the simple reaction which directs a creature to move away from excessive cold or heat, to the more rapid reflex actions brought about by contact. It includes higher complex subconscious impulses such as love and hate, those that govern parental care, as well as the urge to migrate at certain seasons of the year.

Instinct works in many strange and mysterious ways. It tells a bird when and where to build its nest—but the bird is quite unaware why it builds the nest. Very young songbirds in a nest show no fear of a stranger, and make no attempt to escape—not that they could if they tried. These same babies, fully feathered and ready to leave the nest, have somehow acquired the ability to fear and the impulse to flee from danger. Instinct leads the newborn mammal baby to its mother's breast to nurse, and the newly hatched duckling to water. Contrariwise, it keeps the baby chick on dry land.

Instinct keeps an animal in constant readiness to act instantly and to meet any emergency without hesitation. Confronted by the sudden appearance of a mortal enemy, an animal does not make a haphazard dash for safety, but follows a definite method of escape, making all possible use of every advantage. The animal itself may be totally ignorant of why it follows such a course, and is unable to foresee the result of its actions.

When a fox comes bounding along a woodland trail, a squirrel goes up the nearest tree, even though it never saw a fox before in its life. Instinct warns the squirrel of danger and forms its course of action. If it were a rabbit it would make its escape by dashing off on its long legs and not make the mistake of trying to climb a tree. It knows what to do, though it does not always know why.

ANIMALS CAN LEARN

Animals can and do acquire knowledge through learning during a lifetime. A successful life for a mammal is largely dependent on its ability to learn.

Tuition begins in infancy, when a mammal is to no small extent at the mercy of surrounding conditions. It acquires a working intelligence through watching the activities outside itself—their cause and effect.

The comparatively long period of childhood in a mammal, when the brain is pliable, permits a greater development along educational lines than we find in other animals. Under parental tuition the growing young are able to gain considerable useful knowledge that will benefit them in later life. They also learn important details when at play, and practise in fun the particular trades that later will serve them well in making a living. The mother takes her young on excursions into the outside world, where they get first-hand realistic knowledge in the field. Skill comes through practice and by following the example set by the experienced parent.

Curiosity, developed early in life, increases as a mammal learns. It brings a spirit of exploration and a desire for new experiences, enabling an animal to extend its activities into a broader field.

THE CLEVER ONES

Education and intelligence vary in quantity and quality with different kinds of mammals as well as with the individual. Some animals are more adaptable and learn quicker than others; animals that enjoy a long life have a better chance of perfecting their education than those that are short-lived.

Elephants, for example, often show considerable forethought and ability to figure things out for themselves. Those that haul the huge, heavy teak logs down the mountain slopes to the rivers in Burma are known to size up a difficult situation and manoeuvre logs into position without any prompting from the mahout. Some animals even learn to use tools and weapons, although only crudely. Baboons in their native land often pick up stones and throw them with a degree of accuracy at offending strangers. One Barbary ape in a zoo would hurl the contents of its drinking pan into the face of anyone who annoyed it. When the pan was replaced with a stone basin too heavy for the ape to lift, it cupped its hand and with a sudden swing of its arm continued to send a scoop of water at anyone it did not like.

Instinct is a necessity for the existence of all animal life. By their ability to learn, animals can go farther and improve their living conditions, as well as their chances of survival.

ANIMAL FATHERS AND MOTHERS

In the care they give their young, the mammals surpass all other forms of life. It is true that some insects, fishes, reptiles, and amphibians show instinctive concern for the welfare of their eggs and babies, but with enormous numbers it is a matter of chance whether or not the young survive at all. The birds, on the other hand, are famous for the attention they bestow on their offspring; many nestlings are fortunate enough to have the companionship and protection of both mother and father. Still, the mammals as a group show more solicitude than most for the well-being of their babies.

Why should the mammal be a better parent? Earlier we dwelt on the fact that these animals bear their young alive. Many mammal babies are born without sight and are almost naked. For weeks or months they are dependent upon their mother's milk for nourishment. As a rule they could hardly survive without the devoted care of their parents. The babies of the lower animals, in contrast, fend for themselves quite early.

AFFECTION AMONG THE ANIMALS

Man himself is more than just a beast of the field, but he is a mammal. The intimate life of wild animals is much like that of man in many ways.

The feelings of man and beast are perhaps closest during courtship. Both have the same natural instinct to have young and perpetuate their race; both experience passionate feelings of affection for their mate and of hatred for anyone who frustrates their desires.

Female wild animals, like humans, display a share of modesty during courtship and play hard-to-get, but will turn to decoy the male should his interest be lured towards some other female. Most pairs of wild animals, like man, prefer to do their lovemaking in privacy and, at the time, have little interest in anything but each other. Indeed, some species go off by themselves on a prolonged honeymoon.

Most wild animals live a very orderly life. There is a time for courtship and a time to be born, just as there is a time to eat, sleep, and engage in other activities. As a rule, life is so timed that the young are born in the spring of the year, when food is plentiful and there is a whole summer to grow and prepare for the winter.

Wild animals are exceedingly restless during the season of courtship; in fact at this time their behaviour is unpredictable. Some males do not eat for weeks on end but, once the mating season is over, they all settle down to a regular, orderly life. All strife and enmity is forgotten. Warriors that battled in deadly earnest over some comely female, once more become inseparable companions.

HOW THE MOTHER BEARS HER YOUNG

Birth among the wild mammals is much the same as with people. When the wild mother's time draws near, she too begins to feel the natural pangs of labour. As the pain increases, she wanders off alone and seeks some secluded spot to be by herself. Least of all does she need male companionship. She does not shun her mate's company because she fears he will devour the babies—she is simply uncomfortable and in a surly mood. (A dying animal will also go off to meet its end alone.)

When the time comes, the prospective mother lies down on her bed of pain, but she is probably unaware of what is taking place. Once the baby is born, she is on her feet again, with all the maternal care and love of a mother for her newborn child showing in every nervous action. At its first cry she fondly proffers all the solicitude she can.

Being born is comparatively easy and natural with the wild creatures; there is little or no mortality at childbirth. There is no need for a doctor here as is so often the case with domestic animals, where crossbreeding has produced a baby too large for normal birth.

MOST FATHERS GO THEIR OWN WAY

Unlike the birds, few mammals enjoy the care of both parents. Usually only the mother lives in close association with the young during the early stages. This is understandable, since she alone can supply milk. Male sea cows, however, show a marked interest in the young from the very first and will carry the newborn calf around while the mother feeds herself. Males among the herd animals are more typical—they show not the slightest concern for the young.

It is among the carnivores—the flesh-eaters—that we find the father taking a truly dutiful place in family affairs. He is the provider and brings food to the female while she is nursing her cubs or puppies. Later he provides food for the young as well, but he is not permitted in the nursery while they are very little.

THE MOTHER TAKES CHARGE

The young recognize their mother by scent or odour and that is just how their mother recognizes them. Her first duty in many cases is to lick the baby from head to foot. This is a way of establishing ownership. If this ritual were omitted, many a mother would not accept her young under any circumstances.

While the mother's care is largely instinctive, she labours hard on her babies' behalf, and takes earnest precautions to assure their safety.

Frequently she will fight to the death for them. Where a nest or den is disturbed by man, a new nursery is hurriedly put together and the young transported to it without delay. She weans them, accustoming them to the diet of their kind, teaches them how to hunt or get their food in other ways, and in general initiates them into their role in life.

So strong is the maternal instinct in the mammals that females that have lost their young will adopt homeless waifs that have accidentally lost their parents. There is an instance where a cat that had had her kittens destroyed went out into the woods and brought home a family of baby rabbits which she nursed as her own.

It is not uncommon to find young mammals staying with their mother a year or longer. Among some of the more sociable animals, the family may stay together until the youngsters are ready to go off in search of mates of their own. Many a mother, however, drives off her well-grown brood when she is ready to give birth to a new one. Such an action is a matter of instinct of course, but it does serve to protect the helpless new babies from their older brothers and sisters in whom hunger may be stronger than family ties.

This does not necessarily imply that the family bond is irrevocably broken every time a female produces a new family. The breach is frequently bridged over into a lasting friendship that may continue for life. A great-great-grandmother mountain sheep will keep her children and her children's children in her fold, watching over them with motherly care for many years. A pack of wolves is usually all one family, but here the dog wolf takes his place as head of the family. Family relationships among the mammals are closely akin to those that exist among men.

The pioneer spirit of youth, the urge to conquer new fields, to have a home and children of their own is the underlying factor that causes the break-up of most families. Usually the males, in search of a mate, travel farthest afield and entice the young females to elope with them.

WHY ANIMALS LOVE COMPANY

The necessity of being born and cared for in infancy is often at the root of social behaviour in the animal kingdom. Large families carry the social spirit forward towards community life.

[1-M]

Another bird which thrives in an extreme climate is the emperor penguin of Antarctica. Nesting during the long winter, the parents take turns cradling the lone egg, and the chick after it hatches, on their wide feet under a pouch of loose abdominal skin to keep it from the killing cold. Their amusing waddling walk becomes even more ludicrous as they move about with their precious burden.

See page 899

The American robin is one of the outstanding members of the
sweet-singing thrush family. The birds seem to take a rather casual
attitude in selecting the nest site and many of the young are lost,
but since a pair of robins will raise two or three broods a year, the
species flourishes.   *See page 1135*

[1-O]

The Cecropia is a member of the giant silkworm moth family, and is the largest moth in North America north of Mexico; some individuals have been found with a wing expanse of seven inches. It extends over North America east of the Rockies and, like other members of its family (Saturniidae) flies only from dusk into the early part of the night.   *See page 1928*

The Mormon cricket is really a large, cricket-like grasshopper. It was from these agricultural pests that the seagulls delivered the early Mormon settlers in Utah by devouring the insects which were ravaging their first, and sorely needed, crops.

There are, of course, many insects and fishes that never know their parents and yet live together in well-established groups. On the other hand, hyenas and some other animals are rank individualists and cannot tolerate the company of their fellows. Still, we may say that animals that live together in herds, schools, or flocks are in a general sense born to it, and feel ill at ease if separated. When forcibly broken up, a school of fishes, a flock of birds, or a herd of animals will probably join company again as soon as possible.

Many creatures have a genuine desire for intimate companionship with others of their kind, and some develop a personal attachment for a particular individual, sometimes of another species; the friendship of man and his pets is a common example. We can often discern, too, an advantage gained by animals that live together. A musk ox is safe from attack by wolves only so long as it stays with the herd. When danger threatens, a herd of musk oxen form a circle; their horns present a bristling armour, sufficient protection against a whole pack of starving wolves.

In the animal kingdom a sick or old creature, or very young one, cannot as a rule survive on its own for any length of time.

Animals will also perform a common labour to their general advantage. Beavers, working together, can build a great dam, a feat that a single animal would not be capable of.

All this is true not just of mammals, but of other animals. American robins and blue jays, normally enemies, will join forces with sparrows and songbirds to drive away an owl. Tickbirds are friends of the rhinoceroses. Not only do they rid the animals of parasites—they also give the alarm of approaching danger.

PUZZLING HABITS

There are, to be sure, numerous riddles in the social behaviour of animals.

The mountain sheep, for instance, present a rather interesting puzzle. Except during the short breeding season, the sexes never mingle. In British Columbia, the author came upon a herd of twenty-five rams; half a mile away he could see sixteen ewes with their lambs, keeping their distance. This strange segregation of the sexes also takes place among the bats and some other mammals. It is difficult to suggest a reason why it is practised by these groups and not by the rest.

SOCIAL RANK AMONG THE ANIMALS

Social rank is recognized in many groups of animals. Among herd animals there is always a group leader. Usually this is an experienced cow, probably the grandmother of most of the herd. Then there is the master—a herd bull, pompous and self-assured, yet having little authority except at the mating season. Each member of a herd has its place and must wait its turn on the trail. In a pack of wolves, too, one is the leader, a position held by right of might. Others follow in a graduated scale of seniority and valour.

HOW LONG THEY LIVE

All living things, either animal or vegetable, grow old and die. They have their origin in a tiny seed or egg and pass through a regular development to the ordained end. The potential life span varies with the species. It may be long or short according to our standards, but to the individual itself it is a complete, full life cycle.

In a general sense the life span of a species varies with size. The larger it is, the longer it may be expected to live. This is not meant to imply that the biggest animal always lives the longest. The great blue whale is the largest animal that ever appeared on the earth, but there are smaller animals that outlive it. Still, by and large, the rule holds true.

The Oldest Living Thing. No living thing exceeds the giant California redwood in size and age. Sometimes towering four hundred feet skyward, many of these great trees living today were seedlings fifteen hundred years ago. We know that some redwoods actually lived four thousand years. There are many trees, especially among the cone-bearers and oaks, that pass the century mark. On the other hand, we find trees that are old at twenty-five years; some plants pass through a complete life cycle in less than twelve months.

Reptiles and Amphibians are Long-lived. In the animal kingdom, the giant tortoises hold the record for longevity. A Marion's tortoise at Port Louis on Mauritius Island in the Indian Ocean was accidentally killed when it was 152 years old, and there is reason to believe that it might have lived another hundred years. Alligators reach a grand old age; no doubt many of them pass the half-century mark. Some of the Asiatic giant salamanders have lived more than fifty years in captivity. But the tales of toads and newts that have been found in walls or stones where they supposedly survived for indefinite periods of time are discounted nowadays.

Birds. Most birds live considerably more than one year and a few— like some parrots—may survive over fifty years. A swan in Kensington Gardens, London, lived to the ripe old age of eighty-one years.

Fishes. The popular belief that fishes never grow old is discredited by science. As with other animals, the life span of fishes varies roughly with size. A carp will die of old age at fifteen years. The oldest fish of which we have a reliable record is a sixty-year-old European fresh-water catfish, but some of the giant fishes undoubtedly live longer than that, according to James W. Atz of the New York Aquarium. At the other end of the scale there are a number of small fishes with a life span of less than one year.

Insects. Most insects have a life cycle of about one year or less. So far as we know, the seventeen-year cicada is the longest-lived of all the insects but it spends sixteen years and ten months of this time in the ground, developing toward adulthood. Its life as an adult lasts only a few weeks, during which its main business is breeding.

MAMMAL RECORD-HOLDERS

With actual records of over fifty years and possible estimates of up to seventy years, the Asiatic elephant seems to hold the record as the longest-lived of the wild mammals. Among the few other species that may reach or exceed a life of thirty years are the baboon, lion, bear, horse, donkey, rhinoceros, tapir, hippopotamus, and the giraffe, as well as the larger whales.

For their size, the apes, monkeys, and lemurs are the longest-lived of the mammals. The great apes are not fully grown until they are between fifteen and eighteen years of age, and it is not unreasonable to assume that they might live almost as long as man. All we know from individuals in captivity is that the chimpanzee and orang-outang may live to be about twenty-five years of age.

Most cats are in the ten-to-twenty-five-year class. The wild dogs rarely live beyond twenty years, and most cattle, sheep, deer, and antelope—animals that chew the cud—have an average maximum life expectancy of about twenty-five years. Squirrels cannot be expected to live more than fifteen years, and rats and mice not more than six or seven. Shrews and field mice may live about a year or eighteen months, but few ever die of old age.

The untold thousands of years that animals like the cat, dog, horse, and cow have been under human control has neither increased nor decreased their life span. The lives of domestic animals are just as long as would be expected of them had they remained under natural conditions in the wild.

TEETH TELL THE STORY

The length of life in a large majority of mammals has a controlling factor in their teeth. Teeth take a definite time to grow and a less definite, but still limited, time to wear away. When the teeth of a mammal become useless for procuring food, the animal must die.

The loss of its teeth, however, is not quite so drastic an end to the animal as it might seem. Teeth are constructed to last the average life span of a species. Normally the animal would die of old age about the time, or even before, the teeth became useless. The long-lived animals that feed on tough, fibrous grass—the horses, for example—have high-crowned teeth that will take over thirty years to wear down completely.

There is no way known by which we can determine the exact age of a wild mammal. But we can gather a general idea from the wear of its teeth—provided we know the average life span of the species.

WHY EVERY ANIMAL HAS A SCIENTIFIC NAME

There are many living things that look alike but really are different; some that appear to be quite different are close kin. Many animals bear the same popular name; for example, "elk" is a term which for centuries in Europe has been applied to the moose, and in America to what a European would consider a red deer. Clearly, we cannot possibly discuss animals intelligently without first arranging them in a systematic scheme.

The modern method of classification, or taxonomy, is a natural one based on the grouping together of related forms of living things; we judge the closeness of their relationship by the degree of similarity we observe in their form and structure. Thus all living things may be sorted into two groups—plants and animals—called kingdoms.

The kingdom is composed of a number of major divisions, each known as a phylum. Every phylum in turn is split up into classes. Each class may be divided into orders; each order into families; each family into genera (plural of genus); and each genus into species. Sometimes it becomes necessary to form special intermediate groups such as the subphylum, the superclass and the subclass, the super-order and suborder, etc. The scientific name of a creature consists of the names of the genus and species to which it belongs; these are printed in *italic* type.

TRACING THE WOLF

Let us, for example, trace the wolf through the successive groups. It will be a long journey, but we shall get a good idea of the meaning of the terms we have just been talking about. We place the wolf in kingdom Animalia (the animal kingdom), which includes all living things except the plants; phylum Chordata (all animals with a backbone, or vertebral column, and never more than two pairs of limbs), including the mammals, reptiles, amphibians, and fishes; class Mammalia, the mammals (in which all members possess some hair and suckle their young).

At this point we have only reached the mammals. We still have quite a way to go to classify the wolf completely. So, faring onward, we place it in subclass Theria (all living mammals that bring forth their young alive, excluding the egg-laying mammals); order Carnivora (mammals that have sharp teeth for a flesh diet, and toes armed with claws or nails); family Canidae (doglike runners with a long head, unsheathed claws, and long, strong canine teeth); genus *Canis* (typical doglike animals, but excluding the foxes and their relatives); species *lupus* (true wolves).

Now, leaving aside the explanations, let's take the same trip again, this time on an express that will permit us to get a quick picture of the position of a particular kind of wolf in the scientific scheme of things. It is placed in kingdom Animalia, phylum Chordata, class Mammalia, subclass Theria, order Carnivora, family Canidae, genus *Canis*, species *lupus*, subspecies *nubilus*.

Canis lupus nubilus Say, one of the several forms of true wolves, is known to the layman as the buffalo wolf. In scientific literature the name of the person who first described the animal is given following the scientific name—in this instance it was the American zoologist Thomas Say.

In the world today we have eighteen orders of living mammals, 118 families, a minimum of 932 genera, and roughly 3,500 species. The number of species and subspecies listed in 1936 was placed at a total of 14,464, and in round figures 15,000 will serve for the present day. Strange and fascinating creatures they are, almost every one of them. Not the least intriguing are the ones we shall first have a look at, the primitive mammals that lay eggs.

The Spiny Ant-eater and the Duckbill Platypus—Mammals that Lay Eggs

NATURE has a way of surprising us with her creations. We generally think of mammals as animals that bear their young alive, yet in Australia, Tasmania, and New Guinea there are some that actually lay eggs.

These egg-layers are odd creatures with odd names—the spiny ant-eater or echidna, and the duckbill platypus. Their mouths are long and beaklike, like a bird's, but there the resemblance ends; the spiny ant-eater is covered with spines and coarse hair, the duckbill with fur. The one is a burrower, the other a swimmer. Really, they are not so close to the birds as they are to the reptiles, from which they are descended. We consider them the most primitive of living mammals.

The snakelike traits of these animals are striking. We have seen that, like the snakes, they lay eggs. These have thin shells and large yolks, the same as reptile eggs. What is more, the platypus and the spiny ant-eater have the bony shoulder girdle of their reptile ancestors —other mammals discarded it when they rose from the ranks of the lower animals far back in the dim ages of geological time. Other features, too, emphasize the closeness of the relationship.

Still, the spiny ant-eater and the duckbill platypus are mammals, even though we must place them in a special order—the Monotremata, or monotremes. Like their more advanced relatives, they suckle their young with a mammary gland. They have not quite developed a nipple or a teat; the milk comes out of a group of small pores in the skin of the abdomen. All in all, they are strangely fashioned creatures, living symbols of the old and the new in the animal kingdom.

SPINY ANT-EATERS—AUSTRALIA'S "PORCUPINES"

The Five-toed Spiny Ant-eater, or Echidna, *Tachyglossus*, is a shy, small animal native to Australia, Tasmania, and New Guinea. The Australians often call it a "porcupine", for short, sharp spines are mingled with the brownish-grey hair that covers its chubby body. When this creature is on the defensive, the spines present a disturbing prospect to any attacker.

The spiny ant-eater is not in the habit of standing and fighting, however. It has a better way out—it can burrow in the earth with amazing rapidity. The powerful spadelike claws on all four feet can excavate a shaft so fast that it is useless to try to dig the animal out. Oddly enough, it does not dig down head first, as do most burrowing animals, but goes straight down in a horizontal position.

GETTING ITS FOOD

This curious creature is permanently on a soft diet: it has no teeth. Its muzzle looks like nothing so much as a slender beak, and on the end of it is the tubelike opening of the mouth. Ants and termites are the spiny ant-eater's usual fare. It will slash open an ant-hill with its strong claws, then thrust its narrow snout in after the tiny inhabitants. The animal's long, snakelike tongue darts out, snatches them up, and then crushes them against the roof of the mouth. Feeding time is strictly at night; this little mammal stays in hiding by day.

BABY ECHIDNAS

Echidnas are slow breeders. Usually the female lays only a single egg a year. She does not hatch it the way a bird does, for she has her own built-in incubator. This is simply a pocket of skin on her abdomen, rather like a kangaroo's pouch. Inside are the mammary glands, to provide nourishment.

A QUEER-LOOKING "PORCUPINE"

The spiny ant-eater or echidna, native to Australia, is called a porcupine there because of its prickly spines, but it is really uniquely different from that animal. One of the last remaining mammals that lay eggs, it hatches and carries them in a pouch on its abdomen until the babies' spines become uncomfortable. True to its name, it feeds almost solely on ants and termites, catching them with its long tongue and crushing them against its palate.

The egg, soft-shelled, with a parchment-like covering, hatches within a few days, and the baby is carried about in the mother's pouch until its growing spines become a nuisance to her.

Except for size, young and old look alike, and there is no difference in appearance between the sexes.

ANT-EATERS TAME AND WILD

You might suppose the spiny ant-eater would be a strange animal to choose as a pet. Yet it has often been tamed, and shows a friendly nature once it has overcome its shyness.

ONLY ITS BACK IS VISIBLE NOW

Burrowing, the spiny ant-eater thrusts away the dirt with flying claws, but never relaxes the guard of its bristling spines. The soil seems almost to bubble up from around the animal; in a few minutes it is completely out of sight. Of course, the firmer the ground, the longer it takes. See page 24.

ONE OF AUSTRALIA'S STRANGE ANIMALS

Many odd, primitive kinds of mammals survive in Australia, but the duckbill platypus is one of the strangest of all; it lays eggs like its reptile ancestors, but it nurses its young just as modern mammals do. The platypus is at home in Australia's quieter streams and rivers, dwelling in a burrow in a bank. An able swimmer and diver, it feeds on tadpoles, worms, and small fishes. *See page 27.*

[1-1]

A doe stands over her defenceless fawn whose protective camouflage colouring blends with the spring foliage. For its added safety, the fawn at this age has no scent.
See page 710

[1-2]

On the open veldt, where its fleetness of foot is its protection, the zebra is most conspicuous.
See page 662

In the close-grown vegetation of the waterholes where it is at a distinct disadvantage, the zebra's stripes blend with the vertical patterns of sunlight and shadow in the brush.

[1-2a]

Between fifteen and twenty inches is the average length of an echidna. It has only a snip of a tail. The Tasmanian Spiny Ant-eater is larger than its Australian cousin, and its few short spines are almost concealed in its thick woolly fur.

Still larger is the Curve-beaked or Three-toed Spiny Ant-eater, *Zaglossus*, which makes its home in the mountains of New Guinea and Salawati. It reaches a length of about thirty inches, and the beak is exceptionally long.

All the echidnas belong to the family Tachyglossidae ("swift tongue"). They are land animals, with no exceptions.

DUCKBILL PLATYPUSES—A STRANGE COMBINATION

The Duckbill Platypus, *Ornithorhynchus*, is an even stranger egg-laying mammal than the spiny ant-eater. Its scientific name comes from the words *ornis*, meaning "bird", and *rhynchos*, meaning "snout". As its name tells us, the platypus has a bird's beak, or a duck's bill, which it uses for nuzzling in the mud and slush when foraging for worms, aquatic grubs, and other favourite foods. But the bill, instead of being hard and horny, is soft and leathery, and is charged with sensitive nerves.

In contrast to the spiny ant-eater, which has an aversion to water, the platypus is expert at swimming and diving. Its body is admirably adapted for these activities. Its greyish-brown fur is as thick and close as that of an otter, and the tail is flattened like that of a beaver, but well furred. The animal has broadly webbed feet, the front ones furnishing the driving power in the water.

MOTHER DUCKBILL AND HER BABIES

The duckbill breeds once a year. In preparation for her young, the female digs a den laboriously, in the bank of a stream. It is a spacious chamber with a tunnel entrance under water, and also has an air shaft, or ventilator. When the chamber is finished, she lines it with leaves from the gum tree, and shredded grass. She allows no males into her den as she waits for the eggs to arrive.

Finally they come, about fifteen days after mating time. There are generally two of them—one more or less is possible—in a clutch (the name used for the normal number of eggs in a bird's nest). They are soft-shelled and about the size of a pigeon's egg, but rounder. Perhaps to avoid any chance of their being lost in the spacious leafy nest, the two eggs are firmly sealed together side by side. If there are three, they are sealed in a triangle.

Like a bird, the new mother is broody during incubation. For this period of lethargy she locks herself in her underground den by plugging up the entrance with six or eight inches of earth. She does not sit on

A MOST UNUSUAL ANIMAL

The duckbill platypus, found in Australia and Tasmania, is another rare mammal whose young are hatched from eggs. Its body, well suited for swimming, has a bewildering set of features—strong webbed feet, a duck's bill which is soft and sensitive instead of horny, and a flat tail that reminds us of a beaver's.

the eggs like a bird or carry them in a pouch like the echidna, but clutches them to her breast and rolls up into a ball. It takes nine or ten days to complete the incubation.

At first the young platypuses are naked, blind, and helpless, with queer little beaks. The mother platypus, like the mother spiny ant-eater, feeds them on milk secreted by her teatless mammary glands. During these early weeks, the development of the babies is remarkably slow. When two months old, they are covered with short fine fur but must still depend on their mother for body heat, and their eyes have not yet opened. It is at least four months before the youngsters see the light of day. They are amiable little creatures, and play like puppies.

Even at mating time, the male and the female show little or no affection for each other. But they do like company. After the breeding season is over, the platypuses dwell together in a burrow with general living quarters for both sexes.

THE DANGEROUS MALE

Among the platypuses, the male is the deadlier of the species. On his hind foot he bears a horny, hollow spur. Not only is it sharp, but at its base there is a gland containing a poisonous secretion, so that the whole arrangement is rather like the fang of a venomous snake. The spurs are the only means of defence the male platypus possesses, but he wields them with great skill, driving them home with a slashing or stabbing stroke. The wound it produces may be quite serious.

One could hardly call these amusing-looking duck-faced creatures large: full-grown males have a length of about two feet, including the tail, and the females are smaller still. The platypuses form a distinct family (Ornithorhynchidae), dwelling in Australia and Tasmania.

Animals with Pouches—Kangaroos Opossums, and Their Relatives

EVEN a small child knows what animal mother carries her babies about with her in a pouch. Without question, the kangaroo is the best known of the pouched mammals.

Still, we shall find many other fascinating creatures to claim our attention in this group. Not only do the colourful little koalas, the strange Tasmanian devil, the opossums, the wombats, and the bandicoots belong to it, but it also includes such little-known curiosities as pouched mice and moles, and even an animal that can launch itself in the air, the flying phalanger.

These creatures have gone one step higher than the duckbill platypus and the spiny ant-eater on the evolutionary ladder. They bring forth their young alive instead of in eggs, but still in a very incomplete stage of development.

At birth, the hands and feet of these tiny bits of life are well formed, and somehow they manage to scramble through the mother's fur to the pouch on her abdomen. They find it a warm, comfortable haven, equipped with milk taps, and they become inseparably attached to her teats for the rest of their early life. However, they are too young to suck, and so their mother feeds them forcibly by contracting the muscles in her mammary glands. Literally, she injects nourishment down their throats.

We call these animals "marsupials" (order Marsupialia), after a Latin word meaning "pouch". Not all female marsupials have a pouch in which to carry their young, but most of them have some sort of receptacle for this purpose.

WHY THE MARSUPIALS LIVE WHERE THEY DO

One of the strangest facts about the marsupials is connected with where they live. All, with the exception of the opossums of America and a few others, make their home only in Australia and nearby regions. How did they get there? Why don't we find them anywhere else? Their ancestors, already flourishing when the dinosaurs still walked the earth, were spread far and wide over this planet in remote times. They were among the commonest of the early mammals.

At the time the marsupials came into being, Australia was joined to other large land-masses. The pouched animals—an opossum seems to have been the first of them—were easily able to enter it. But, later, great geological changes took place. Australia became separated from neighbouring areas, an island continent.

In all other places, new and more advanced kinds of mammals developed and grew to be dominant. These were the forebears of the animals that cover the earth today—the placentals, which bear their young alive without need for the protection of pouches. The new-comers wiped out the ancient marsupials almost everywhere. In the Americas, a few managed to hold out: the opossums. In Australia, however, the marsupials were protected by a "wall of water", and life remained easy for them till the coming of man.

PRIMITIVE ANIMALS

Among the marsupials, we find eaters of flesh as well as eaters of plants and insects. Teeth are numerous—often there are more than forty-four. Milk teeth are a rarity, however. The marsupials possess a double womb, and generally lack a placenta, the organ by which our "modern" mammals nourish the young in the mother's body. It is for this reason that marsupial babies are so undeveloped at birth. These animals are not outstanding for their intelligence; on the whole, their brains are small.

OPOSSUMS—AMERICA'S ONLY MARSUPIALS

The Common or Virginia Opossum, *Didelphis,* the only marsupial found in the United States, is at home from South America to New England. It looks rather like an oversized rat, and is credited with being the stupidest creature in the American woods. Its highest show of animation is a silly snarl. It is bad-tempered, unresponsive and indifferent to company.

Prowling about in the cold damp woods and swamps in the gloom of the night, sometimes the opossum is caught in a flash of light. For a moment its eyes shine like two red balls of fire. It is so shocked at being confronted with danger that its limited mental capacity is overwhelmed. The opossum suffers a temporary paralysis, falling into a state of coma. To all outward appearances the creature is dead. It is this curious behaviour on its part which has given rise to the popular phrase "playing 'possum".

So far as we may judge, the ambitions of the opossum are simple ones: to find a snug warm nest safe from beasts of prey, to multiply its kind, and to fill its belly. Everything edible is food for the opossum—roots, fruits, insects, and small mammals. It is one of man's helpers, for it is a great destroyer of rodents. But some of its nightly wanderings take it into barnyards, where it cannot resist the temptations offered by young birds and eggs. And so, to its misfortune, it runs foul of farmers.

Hunting the opossum is a popular sport, and the roasted flesh is considered a delicacy. A long coat of grizzled hair mixed with fur covers the animal, an added lure for the hunter; this fur has considerable commercial value.

——BIRTH AND DEATH AMONG THE OPOSSUMS. With their numerous enemies, both human and animal, opossums seldom die of old age. Seven years is about as long as they live.

UGLY, STUPID, AND ADDICTED TO FAINTING SPELLS

The common or Virginia opossum is considered unattractive, unlovable, and stupid. The familiar expression "playing 'possum" comes from this animal's peculiar habit of falling into a coma when it is suddenly exposed to danger. It is one of the very few marsupials living outside the Australian region. Other opossums dwell in South America.

In northern latitudes the opossum breeds once a year, and tragedy is often present from the very first. The female may bear as many as twenty offspring, tiny mites hardly larger than a bee. About half are doomed at birth, for a strange reason.

The mother rarely has more than thirteen teats, or "feeding stations", frequently only eleven. The first comers make haste to reach her pouch and establish themselves at these sources of food. Each fixes itself to a teat, to remain fastened there for weeks. Late arrivals find all the places taken. They starve to death. Still, the breed owes its very existence to the fact that it is so prolific.

The surviving babies grow rapidly. In about a week they are some ten times their size at birth. When they grow too large to fit into the mother's pouch, they climb on to her back. Here, their feet and tail entwined securely in her long hair, they stay fixed much of the time, till they are ready to make their own way in the world at the age of two months.

When full grown, the Virginia opossum is hardly an attractive creature. It is about the size of a house cat (two feet or more from its nose to the tip of its tail) but its legs are much shorter, and it has a longish snout. Large dark eyes shine in its white face. It has more teeth than the average land mammal. Its furry, greyish-white body weighs about eight pounds, and ends in a naked ten-inch tail.

——A REMARKABLE TAIL. The Virginia opossum is an able tree climber, and often sleeps in the branches. Its hind feet as well as its forefeet have an opposable digit—that is, the great toe is formed like the thumb on the human hand. Its long, scaly tail has a prehensile (grasping) tip; the opossum can curl it into a tight hook and use it as a "fifth hand" to carry a bunch of leaves or hang from the branch of a tree.

The opossum's tail developed as a grasping instrument in South America, where the group originally came from. Tails of this type are well developed in many widely separated tree-living mammals of that continent, among them certain monkeys, ant-eaters, rodents and carnivores. We do not find this extra anchorage so completely perfected by mammals elsewhere, except to some extent in the marsupials of the Australian region.

——"THE INCREDIBLE MOTHER". Strange as it may seem, the American opossum was the first of the marsupials encountered by western civilization. It was discovered by the Spanish explorer Pinzón in 1500. In fact, it was presented at the court of Ferdinand and Isabella, where it created quite a sensation.

Knowing the opossum for the humble creature it is, we find it hard to understand the amazement it produced among the early Spaniards. They described this new kind of animal as a frightful beast with a face like a fox, the tail of a monkey, ears like a bat and human hands.

Below, on the belly, they said, it has a second belly hanging down like a great sack or pouch in which the animal carries its young. To them it was "the incredible mother".

"Opossum" is an American Indian name. In the language of the Algonquians it means "white animal". Earlier we saw that the Virginia opossum is the only pouched mammal dwelling in the United States. All other American marsupials make their home in Central and South America. The opossums belong to the family Didelphidea ("double womb").

SOME INTERESTING OPOSSUMS OF
CENTRAL AND SOUTH AMERICA

The Yapok, *Chironectes*, is unique among the opossums or, for that matter, among the marsupials—it is the only member of its order really at home in the water. Because of this peculiarity, we often call it the Water Opossum. It even derives its name from a river, the Oyapok, in Guiana.

The yapok is smaller than the Virginia opossum—its head and body are twelve inches long, its tail about fourteen. It is a handsomer animal by far, and is noted in particular for the striking colour pattern of its fur. Almost black in hue, its coat is broken by transverse bands of silvery white, producing a unique marbled effect. The fur is soft, but dense enough to shed water.

——THE YAPOK GOES FISHING. The yapok's hind feet are broadly webbed for swimming. It can swim and dive with the facility of an otter. Its skill in the water is proved by the fact that it has been taken in eel and fish traps set deep down in swift streams.

The jungles of South America are the home of the yapok. It may be found as far south as Paraguay, as far north as Mexico. A night prowler, it hunts its prey in the impenetrable darkness of the tropical forests. Here, amid the constant chorus of frogs and chirping insects, it swims along freshwater streams and lakes, searching for the shellfish, crayfish, and other forms of water life on which it feeds.

——THE YAPOK'S DEN. It is not hard to recognize a yapok's den in the jungle. Tracks of webbed feet and fingers on well-trodden runways lead to a hole in the ground. It is usually in a bank, just above water level. Around it, sticking in the mud, you will find the remains of crayfish, bits of fins, and fish heads. As a temporary resting-place, the animal may also make a surface nest of leaves or grass on the ground.

The female yapok produces about five or six babies in a litter. Provided with a perfect pouch, she carries them about with her on her daily excursions in the water for food. When too big to fit in the mother's pouch, the little yapoks must stay at home, but the family ties are not broken until they are well grown.

A WATER-LOVING OPOSSUM

The only opossum that has a special liking for water is the yapok or water opossum, found in the South American jungle. This animal is an excellent swimmer and diver, very much like the otter. The yapok is smaller and more attractive than its relative, the Virginia opossum; its deep black coat is banded with stripes of silvery white.

The Four-Eyed Opossum, *Philander,* owes its common name to an oddity in its appearance. On its head are four yellowish-white spots that resemble eyes. Except for this and its smaller size (head and body are about ten inches, tail eleven) and short close fur, it rather resembles its cousin the Virginia opossum.

——A COURAGEOUS OPOSSUM. *Philander* is common in tropical America, from Vera Cruz, in Mexico, south to Brazil. It favours forested country from sea-level up to four thousand feet. The natives call it the *zorro*, which means "fox" in Spanish. They esteem it because it is a plucky little fellow, always ready to defend itself against great odds. Such a show of spirit is a rarity in the Virginia opossum.

——THE MOTHER IS EVER WATCHFUL. The female four-eye is a builder. She weaves a neat globular nest of dried leaves and grasses in thick foliage, where it will be hidden from her enemies. She makes it about a foot in diameter, with the chamber roughly the size of her body. Here she bears her family of five or six young.

Like other opossums, this one carries her babies with her wherever she goes. Mother four-eye is for ever on the alert, and will slip silently away from her snug retreat at the least sign of danger, bearing her babies to safety.

It is not uncommon for small opossums to be carried away in bunches of bananas, and on occasion a much-perplexed zorro has found itself far from home in a New York fruit market, surrounded by a wondering crowd of spectators.

The Woolly Opossum, *Caluromys*, is a beautiful, ornate creature, distinguished by its golden tawny back and light-coloured withers mark. The extraordinary tail, heavily furred for one-third of its length with the rest naked, measures about twenty inches—just about twice as long as the animal's head and body.

The woolly opossum makes its home in the woodland, from Mexico to Paraguay. The most tree-loving of the opossums, it spends the greater part of its life in the top branches of forest giants. Fond of privacy, it builds its leafy nest in thick foliage at a considerable distance from the ground. Because it has rather small and weak teeth, it lives chiefly on a diet of pulpy fruits and small insects.

The Murine or Mouse Opossum, *Marmosa*, is called "murine" because if its colour—the word means "mouse grey". Actually its coat may vary from pale grey to tawny. The creature is ratlike in size, measuring up to six inches in head-and-body length; its naked tail may be twice as long. Across its eyes it usually has a distinctive black facial mask.

The murine opossum is a forest-lover. It spends much of its time in the trees, hunting for beetles, moths, and sleeping butterflies. It is also fond of ripe fruits, especially the soft pulpy kind such as bananas. Like most of the American opossums it is strictly a night prowler.

This 'possum often uses a bird's nest for a dwelling, but it may build its own nest of green leaves far from the ground. In their leafy home, the opossum family finds a measure of safety from the usual host of flesh-eaters ready to devour it—cats, wild dogs, and large snakes—but it is still exposed to its most dreaded foes, the owls.

——MARSUPIAL WITHOUT A POUCH. Although the mother murine opossum has no pouch, her babies do not suffer any special disadvantage.

AN OPOSSUM OF CENTRAL AND SOUTH AMERICA

The murine or mouse opossum, shown here on the ground, spends many of its hours in the trees. We find it in forests all the way from Central Mexico to Patagonia; there are no fewer than forty-nine species and one hundred subspecies of this common creature. Named because of its mouse-grey colour, it is rat-sized and often has a black mask on its face.

They cling to her with their tiny feet and mouths as though for dear life. So strong is their hold that if you tried to pick up one of these tiny mites you would have to lift the mother, too.

——A MOTHER'S TRICKS. Sometimes a baby may be separated from its mother. She does not go over and pick it up with her teeth as a rat would, but noses the infant under her so it can grasp her fur. A mother has been seen to toss her baby in the air with her snout and catch it on her back.

——USEFUL PETS. These small animals have their uses. When taken young, the murine opossum makes a nice pet. It is very valuable about the house in tropical countries, for it devours the cockroaches that lurk in every dark corner. It catches mice with the skill of a house cat.

——A GREAT RACE. The range of these little opossums extends from central Mexico to Patagonia, and from sea-level to eight thousand feet. They are a great race: there are forty-nine species and one hundred subspecies of murine opossums.

Of these, one of the largest is Alston's Marmosa, of Central America and Colombia—it measures seventeen inches overall. The smallest is the Least Murine Opossum of the province of Formosa, Argentina; this dwarf is only two and one-half inches in head-and-body length, with a tail equally long.

Some species breed three times a year and have up to ten or eleven young in a litter. Others apparently have up to nineteen—at least that is the largest number of teats they possess.

Australia's Pouched Mammals

Except for the American opossums we have just been looking at, all the marsupials live in Australia and the islands of the South Pacific. In fact, we find few mammals but marsupials in this region. The herd animals of the plains and grasslands are marsupials; the equivalents of the rabbits, moles, cats, and wolves are marsupials. There is even a marsupial tiger.

Protected by the vast expanse of the Pacific and neighbouring seas for millions of years, the pouched animals led a secure existence in the isolation of their island homes. This marsupial paradise began to draw to an end with the coming of man. Besides killing large numbers of animals for their fur, he brought in the cat and the dog; these two have taken their toll. To make matters worse, imported rabbits and sheep graze bare the plains where the pouched mammals used to feed.

Today the native animals are definitely on the way out. Some species of the marsupial flesh- and insect-eaters (family Dasyuridae, or "bushy tails") have been exterminated almost completely.

MARSUPIAL FLESH- AND INSECT-EATERS

The Thylacine, Marsupial Wolf, or Marsupial Tiger, *Thylacinus*, is the largest of the flesh-eating marsupials. It is easily recognized: it is about the size of a collie and has sixteen to eighteen distinctive chocolate-brown stripes running across the rear of its back. Wiped out in Australia, this savage creature is making a last-ditch stand in Tasmania.

The marsupial wolf lies up during the daylight hours in a rocky lair. It waits till dusk before it ventures out to hunt in the valleys and plains. Here, under normal conditions, it tracks down wallabies and other Tasmanian marsupials. When it cannot find them, as is the common case today, it preys upon flocks of domestic sheep and poultry. For these depredations it has a black mark against its name.

WOLF, DOG, OR TIGER?

Thylacine, marsupial wolf, or marsupial tiger are three of the names by which this largest of the flesh-eating pouched animals is known. It preys upon wallabies, other Tasmanian marsupials, or sheep and poultry. Its head can easily be taken for a dog's, while its brown stripes remind one of the zebra.

The marsupial wolf is a formidable foe. Although not so swift as a true northern wolf or even a domestic dog, it is a tireless runner and follows its prey until the victim is exhausted.

Man is the marsupial wolf's chief enemy. When hard pressed by danger, according to reports, the animal seems to abandon its normal running gait; it speeds away in a series of kangaroo-like leaps. Normally it will not attack a human being unless it has been cornered. It is more than a match for the average dog. With its back to a wall, the "wolf" can fight off a whole pack.

——A FEROCIOUS FEMALE. The female marsupial wolf has a pouch large enough to carry four babies. In guarding them, she shows the same maternal fortitude we see in other animals.

On one occasion, a traveller who was about to cross a creek by means of a fallen tree found his way barred by a thylacine, undoubtedly a female. She barked at him fiercely, uttering the guttural, cough-like sound this animal makes when alarmed or excited. Finally, with some difficulty, the traveller made his way to the opposite bank. There, under a tree fern, he found two marsupial wolf babies in a nest of dried fronds.

The marsupial wolf's scientific name, *Thylacinus cynocephalus*, is very appropriate; it means "pouched animal with a dog's head". On this "dog's head" the muzzle is fairly long and pointed; the ears are broad and rounded. In colour the thylacine is brown. Its chocolate stripes begin just behind the shoulders; they increase in length until they reach the thighs, then decrease and disappear a short distance down the tail. Because of them the animal is also known as the Zebra Opossum or Zebra Wolf. It has a total length of some sixty-five inches, including a tail twenty inches long.

The Tasmanian Devil, *Sarcophilus*, despite its forbidding name, is no more fearful than any of the other flesh-eating mammals. It is a chubby, short-legged creature not more than about three feet long. Superficially it resembles a small bear. Its ferocious expression and jet black colour earned it the popular name of "native devil".

Like the marsupial wolf, the Tasmanian devil once roamed over much of Australia. Nowadays, however, it survives only in Tasmania. It is a land animal, but haunts the borders of rivers or beaches. There it finds a variety of food such as rats, mice, frogs, crabs, and the like. Most of its natural prey has been greatly reduced in numbers, and it has little alternative but to raid the sheep ranges and chicken farms. Its powerful jaws and muscular neck enable it to maintain a stranglehold on a victim considerably larger than itself.

The call of the "devil" at night can hardly be said to cheer the lonely traveller. It is an eerie sound: a low, yelling growl followed by a snarling cough. It has not helped the animal's sinister reputation.

The Tasmanian devil mates in March and April; the young generally come in May. About a month after the babies are born, the she-devil builds a nest in the rocks for them; they are now too big to be carried around in her pouch and would be a hindrance when hunting. The little "devils" are good tree-climbers—more so than the adults, which can only go up a slanting trunk.

——NOT SO BLACK AS IT LOOKS. People often credit the marsupial devil with an untamable disposition. Still, its character is not so black as its appearance. Taken young and reared in captivity, it makes an excellent pet. It is as frolicsome as a kitten, but more affectionate. It washes its face with its paws like a house cat but uses both hands at the same time, fitting them together. After licking them thoroughly, it rubs them over its head.

NOT SO SINISTER AS ITS NAME

The Tasmanian devil was given its name because of its deep black colour and forbidding look. Yet it is simply another one of the flesh-eating marsupials, with nothing especially sinister in its habits except an appetite for domestic animals. See how appropriately powerful are its head and neck. The animal is seldom seen, for it is almost extinct.

This bearlike animal is not like a bear in every way. Most bears have only a stump of a tail; the Tasmanian devil's may be a foot long. Although very powerful, the creature has its strength centred forward; its hindquarters are noticeably weak. Its coat of coarse black hair is splashed with irregular blotches of white on the rump, throat, and shoulders.

The Marsupial Cat, *Dasyurus*, looks more like a weasel or a skunk than a cat. Despite its small size—it is less than a foot long, with a bushy tail almost the same length—it is a bold, fearless hunter, endowed with considerable intelligence. It makes its home in Australia and New Guinea.

Like a skunk, the marsupial cat hunts its prey at night. It feeds to a large extent on lizards, rats, mice, and insects. It will raid poultry pens, and for that reason is disliked by the settlers.

——STALKING ITS PREY. The marsupial cat is an accomplished bird-stalker. It will creep up on a heron with all the skill and stealth of a tiger. When the bird's head goes down and its attention is elsewhere,

A HUNTER OF CONSIDERABLE REPUTE

The marsupial cat hunts down lizards, rats, mice, insects, and especially birds, with great cunning and skill. By a strange chance of nature, many of these cats do not last long after birth. The female may bear twenty-four at one time, yet can feed only the half-dozen her six teats will accommodate. A life of persecution awaits the babies that survive.

the cat moves quickly forward. When the heron raises its head to look about, the cat stops dead in its tracks. Thus, with a sharp eye on the bird's movements, it advances and halts by turns, until it has drawn close enough for the final spring.

The marsupial cat is as much at home in the trees as on the ground; it will make its den in a hollow tree or in a crevice in the rocks. It sleeps during the day.

[1-3]

Semi-albino possum. Albinos of any species are very rare in Nature. Lacking protective colouring, they are easy victims of predators. Often they are murdered by their own group simply because they are ''different'', and should one manage to attain maturity, it has difficulty finding a mate—for the same reason.
See page 50

Comparison of a new-born possum with a small wasp. Possums are born at a very early stage of embryonic development, but somehow these tiny mites make their way to the mother's pouch, where they rapidly complete their "pre-natal" growth. *See page 48*

[1-5]

Too large for their mother's pouch, baby possums cling fast to the long hair of her back, venturing only short distances away, until they are about two months old. *See page 48*

[1-6]

At the age of two months, the young possum is
''on his own''.
See page 48

Climbing, the possum reaches for a branch with
a ''fifth hand''—its prehensile, or grasping, tail.
See page 48

[1-6a]

——DOOMED AT BIRTH. Nature, as we shall see again and again, often produces more animal babies than can possibly survive. Seldom do we find a more startling example of this than among the marsupial cats: the female, although equipped with a well-developed pouch, possesses only six teats, yet she may bear as many as twenty-four young at a time. Eighteen of these are doomed at birth.

There are several different species of marsupial cats. The typical animal has reddish or olive-brown fur, profusely dotted with large and small white spots on the head and over the body.

MARSUPIAL MICE

Among the animal oddities that dwell in Australia, Tasmania, and New Guinea, not the least remarkable are the marsupial mice. Miniatures of their kind, they vary in size from about nine to sixteen inches, and usually have a tail shorter than their head and body. Most will feed on anything they can find: insects, small animal life, eggs, and vegetable matter. Some, like the Vampire Marsupial, live in trees; others— the "Jerboa", the Marsupial Rat, and the Mulgara—dwell on the ground in desert wastes.

The Jerboa Marsupial Mouse, *Antechinomys*, is particularly note-worthy. It has greatly enlarged legs and feet on which it hops around like a mouse-sized kangaroo. Its face is pointed, with long whiskers on the snout; it also has three or four long whisker-like hairs that extend backward from its wrist to well behind its elbow. Its ears are enormous, and it has a long tail tufted at the tip. All in all, it presents a curious spectacle.

This strange little creature lives in holes in the ground in Australia. Its diet consists in the main of insects but now and then it attracts and kills mice.

The Crest-tailed Marsupial Rat, *Dasyuroides*, of the sandy desert regions of central Australia, is nearly as big as a house rat. Its fur is reddish brown, and its tail has a crest both below and above. The animal lives in burrows on the sandy and stony tablelands. Although said to be a night prowler, the crest-tail has a fondness for basking in the warm sunshine.

The Brush-tailed Phascogale, *Phascogale*, a beautiful blue-grey bushy-tailed marsupial rat, is active in the trees; for this reason and its general appearance it was known as a squirrel to the early colonists.

The brush-tailed phascogale has some of the American pack rat's habits of collecting. This has been responsible for some curious incidents. For example, once a member of a group of foresters found that a banknote was missing from his possessions. He could not help but suspect his friends; for a while a strained feeling prevailed in the foresters' camp. Finally the men felled a tree near by. They were amazed to find the banknote neatly stowed away in a phascogale's nest in the tree.

The Vampire Marsupial, as this phascogale is often called, feeds mostly on insects. Occasionally it kills and eats larger animals as well. It serves a useful purpose in keeping under control the hordes of rats and mice that have established themselves in Australia. Reports have it that the little marsupial follows plagues of rodents, putting in full time in an effort to reduce their numbers.

In a poultry pen the brush-tail will kill more fowls than it can eat. Because of this habit, many Australians mistakenly believe that it only sucks the blood from the throat of its victims.

The Crest-tailed Pouched Mouse, *Dasycercus*, a redoubtable creature of the desert region of Central Australia, is only the size of a large mouse. It is reddish brown in colour, and has a crest of stiff hairs at the tip of its tail; its nose is long and pointed.

The mulgara, as it is frequently called, is fearless, and ferocious for its size. It will attack and kill a large mouse and devour most of it, starting at the head.

Indeed, common mice are important to the prosperity of the mulgara. On several occasions it has multiplied in an astonishing manner during mouse plagues; at other times its numbers may dwindle. In the 1905 mouse plague, human intervention could not check the increase of the rodent spoilers. Then this ravenous little flesh-eater went into action. In a short time it had cleared entire districts of the plague.

Actually, the mulgara is not so fierce as this account may suggest. Many consider it an affectionate little creature. Certainly it behaves like one toward its own kind. Mulgars love warmth. They bask in the sunshine, stretched out in lizard-like fashion with their heads resting on each other's backs.

The female usually has about seven babies in a litter, but she has no pouch. Nature offers many strange sights, but few excel this humble one: Mother Mulgara staggering along in search of food with seven youngsters hanging from her nipples.

The Banded Ant-eater, White-banded Bandicoot, or Numbat, *Myrmecobius*, is about the size of a large house rat but looks more like a squirrel, bushy tail and all. (Although it spends much of its time in the forest, apparently it does not, like the squirrel, climb trees.) It has been encouraged in Australia because it serves as a control against termites, but under natural conditions it is fast disappearing; it is now found only in the south-western part of the continent.

Most other ant-eaters do not have any teeth; the banded ant-eater, however, has even more than the average mammal. Yet it prefers to let this fine equipment remain idle—it does not chew its food, but swallows it whole. From the sharp-pointed face an extendible tongue darts out, and quickly licks up ants and termites. With its long claws it can dig into cracks and crevices and hook them out, too.

The banded ant-eater travels about in broad daylight as well as at night. Rather slow in action, it moves along in a succession of short leaps; at intervals it rests on its haunches to have a look round. Many birds and animals find it an easy prey.

Shy and inoffensive in its ways, the banded ant-eater will not attempt to bite even when caught. In captivity, it will lap up sweetened milk by the rapid motion of its long tongue. The extreme extent of its vocal powers is a snuffling grunt.

The female banded ant-eater has no pouch. She produces four young, and these have only the protection of her coarse hair. The aborigines claim that she makes her den in a hollow tree, where she leaves her young when they are too large to carry around.

The banded ant-eater is about seventeen inches long (including seven inches of bushy tail). It wears a coat of rather coarse, harsh, brightly coloured fur. Six or seven white stripes run across its rich reddish-brown back.

MOLES WITH POUCHES

The Marsupial Mole, *Notoryctes*, of Australia, is in no way related to the common mole. Still, there is a striking likeness in size and form.

Its forefeet, or hands, are greatly enlarged and end in strong claws, wonderful tools for excavating tunnels in the earth. Its eyes and ears are small and poorly developed. The tip of the marsupial mole's nose and its tail are naked and covered with coarse skin; its coat of close soft fur is like the common mole's, but the colour is yellowish white instead of almost black.

——THE MAD SCRAMBLE OF LIVING. Moles in general expend a tremendous amount of energy, and the marsupial mole is no exception. It must feed every hour, day and night; its life is little more than a continuous search for food.

The marsupial mole eats with fevered haste, and will devour a handful of worms in a remarkably short time. Having satisfied its hunger for the moment, it will abruptly fall fast asleep. It wakens with a start and continues on its mad scramble for more food. It is an animal that lives in alternate spasms of great activity and complete rest.

——AN ANIMAL THAT "FLOWS ALONG". This little creature makes its burrows about three inches below the surface. It leaves no permanent tunnel. At regular intervals it will break the surface soil and stick its nose out to breathe more freely. Above ground, it moves with a rapid shuffling motion—it seems almost to flow along.

We know little or nothing about the breeding habits of the marsupial mole. Like most marsupials the female has a pouch in which to carry her young. The moles of this type make up the family Notoryctidae ("southern diggers").

BANDICOOTS—"BADGERS WITH POUCHES"

"Badger with a pouch"—that is the meaning of the family name of the bandicoots (Peramelidae). They are curious little animals, some as small as a chipmunk, others as big as a rabbit. All have long, narrow feet with long claws, and usually a long, pointed face; most possess a rather short tail. Their hind legs are enlarged so that they can hop around like kangaroos; their forefeet and claws are suited for digging in the ground in search of larvae and insects.

—— A STRANGE WAY OF FIGHTING. The bandicoot is a fighter with techniques of combat all its own. Two bandicoots will not battle face to face; they prefer to chase one another around. The assault is made by jumping and simultaneously striking with the powerful hind feet.

A well-placed blow cuts out a batch of hair and skin from the victim's back.

In killing its prey the bandicoot uses a like technique. Having hunted down a worm or a mouse, the bandicoot kneads it to a pulp on the ground with rapid strokes of its forefeet and then eats it. Its food, for the most part, consists of insects, but it will also eat roots, fruits, and vegetables.

ITS EARS GIVE IT A RABBITY LOOK

The rabbit bandicoot's or bilby's mark of distinction is its rabbit ears, which, together with its long, painted face, give it an unusual appearance. Nevertheless, it is a true bandicoot or "badger with a pouch". Bandicoots are pugnacious animals, but they never fight face to face. Instead, they pursue one another in circles, jumping and hitting out with their long hind feet. Thanks to their sturdy claws, they can dig with amazing speed.

The bandicoots are well known and widely spread over Australia, Tasmania, Papua, and New Guinea. The Rabbit Bandicoot, or Bilby, is the oddest looking, with its large, leathery, rabbit-like ears and long, pointed snout. The Spiny Bandicoot has sharp spines mixed with its fur. And the Pig-footed Bandicoot, now a rare species, gets its name from its hooflike paws. Some species have ornate stripes on the lower back.

The Common Bandicoot, *Perameles*, is a slender, grey-brown animal with fairly large pointed ears and a sharp, pointed face. It is about twenty inches long, tail and all. The Australians call it a "thill" or "moncat" and consider its flesh delicate and excellent food.

By day this little marsupial seeks shelter in hollow logs or crevices in the rocks; sometimes it will construct a rough nest. At night it becomes extremely active, hunting for insects and digging worms out of the ground with its long, sharp claws. When alarmed, it will spring high in the air.

May and June are breeding time for the common bandicoot. The female produces two young, which she carries about in her well-formed pouch. She is a little smaller than the male, but is coloured like him.

There are a number of species of common bandicoots native to Australia and Tasmania. We can easily distinguish them from one another by the characteristics mentioned in their common names: the Long-nosed Bandicoot, the Orange-backed or Desert Bandicoot, the Tasmanian Barred Bandicoot, and Western Barred Bandicoot.

AUSTRALIAN POSSUMS, GLIDERS, AND KOALAS

The Cuscus, *Phalanger*, is a rather large, lazy, furry animal with a long whip of a tail which it uses to hold on to things. Like all of the phalangers, gliders and possums that make up its family (Phalangeridae —these are all "opossums" of a sort, but are here called "possums", to differentiate them from the American family), the cuscus spends most of its time in the trees. It has a light-coloured patch on its rump from sitting and sleeping for long hours in forked branches.

Between sunrise and sunset the cuscus remains hidden in hollow trees or conceals itself in masses of vegetation. During the hours of darkness it comes to life. But even now activity is by no means its strong point. It presents a perfect picture of slow motion as it inches through the trees, feeding steadily on leaves. According to reports it catches and eats birds and small mammals.

The cuscus gives off a foul odour, which makes it an easy animal to detect. Any disturbance will bring a ceaseless chatter of protest from it. It is said to be simple to capture for the reason that, stared at incessantly for some time, it will suspend itself by its powerful tail and hang this way until it drops to the ground from fatigue.

Northern Queensland and New Guinea, the Celebes, the Solomons, and a few other islands of the South Pacific are the home of the cuscuses. They dwell farther east than most other marsupials, but are not very common anywhere.

The cuscus is known as the *kapune* to the natives of New Ireland, and as *coes-coes* to the Amboyna natives. Full grown, its body measures from fifteen inches to twice that length; the grasping tail adds another fifteen inches to it. The animal is much sought after for its flesh by the natives everywhere. They roast it whole over peat fires.

The Spotted Cuscus, *Spilocuscus*, is not only a strikingly coloured creature—it is one of the relatively few mammals in which the sexes differ distinctively in colour pattern. Basically, they vary from brownish

ONLY THE MALE IS SPOTTED

The male and female spotted cuscus, unlike most other mammals, each have a different colour pattern: the male's back is spotted with white or grey marks but the female's is completely unspeckled. The cuscus passes its days sitting quietly and snugly in trees, becoming energetic only at night. Its long tail is a fine grasping tool.

to greyish white. On the back the dark-coloured males are spotted with white; the light ones are spotted with grey. But the colour of the female's back is uniform and unbroken by any markings.

The female cuscus has a well-developed pouch in which she carries her two to four young. Rarely do we discover her without at least one baby in her pouch, and so we assume that she breeds the year round.

The spotted cuscus is at home in New Guinea, New Britain, the Admiralty Islands, and Cape York. In its ways it reminds us of its cousin *Phalanger*. It spends the day curled up in the fork of a tree among thick foliage, and its motions are slow in daylight. The rounded face, thick woolly coat, and grasping tail (this last item makes up about half of the spotted cuscus's length of three feet, six inches) give the animal a monkey-like appearance, but its slow movements are anything but simian. It does wake up and become more active at night.

The Australian or Vulpine Possum. *Trichosurus*, is in Australia the commonest and most familiar of all the marsupials. You can quickly tell this handsome furry little fellow from the others by its thick brush of a tail, its pointed face, and long ears. As a matter of fact, it was these features that suggested the name "vulpine" (foxlike) opossum to the early naturalists.

———A VERSATILE MARSUPIAL. The Australian possum is the most adaptable of the marsupials. Although built for a life in the trees, it thrives in almost treeless plains; it may make its den in rabbit holes as readily as in the upper branches of the giant gum trees. It is at home even in the suburbs of large cities, just like the grey squirrel in America. We do not see it about during the daylight—indeed, strong light is harmful to its eyes.

———PARALYSED WITH FEAR. Insects are the staple diet of the Australian possum. It will also eat a variety of leaves and vegetable matter and, on occasion, meat, but it is not an habitual killer. Its archenemy is said to be the great monitor lizard or goanna, which climbs the trees to attack it in its retreat. The possum is so paralysed with fear that it makes no attempt to escape. Indeed, on close acquaintance, this creature proves to be rather stupid. Even newly caught adults show little resentment to captivity so long as they get enough to eat.

The brush-tail possum, as the Australians often call it, breeds in May or June—usually only once a year. While the female has two teats, rarely will more than one young be found in her pouch at a time. The baby is ready to leave this warm shelter in September, and family ties are usually broken in November.

Brush-tails are attractive creatures. The various species range in colour from pale grey to blackish or reddish brown. On an average, they are about thirty inches long (one-third of this is the flat, bushy tail). The underside of the tail is naked for grasping; the ears are erect and pointed.

——A VALUABLE FUR-BEARER. The beautiful, thick close fur of this animal made it for a long time of great economic importance as a fur-bearer. There was a large export trade in the skins. The animals are now protected by the authorities from indiscriminate slaughter.

The Sugar Glider or Flying Phalanger, *Petaurus,* is a small, attractive, downy-furred creature with large, soft eyes and a long, bushy tail. Its home is in Australia, New Guinea, and the neighbouring islands, where it is known as the flying squirrel. Actually, it is not a true flying squirrel, though the resemblance is fairly close.

IT GLIDES THROUGH THE AIR

The sugar glider is a pretty little animal that lives in trees and is remarkably adept at gliding from one to another. Stretching taut the membranes attached to the sides of its body and its limbs, it catapults itself from the top of the tree. When landing, it twists its body upward in order to break its speed and it reaches the ground upright.

Home to the sugar glider must always be on high. This little animal makes its nest or den of leaves either in the crotch of a tree or inside a hollow gum tree, about twenty-five feet or more above the ground. It is a rather friendly creature, and half a dozen adults may take up companionable quarters in the same den in a hollow tree.

The sugar glider is active only by night. Insects, fruits, and leaves are its favourite foods. It has a curious habit of wrapping its tail around a bundle of leaves or twigs and carrying them to its nest. It is partial to blossoms of the manna gum tree, and also licks the leaking sweet sap of this tree, a habit which has earned it its name.

——How the Glider Travels. The sugar glider, we have said, also goes by the name of "flying squirrel". While it cannot actually fly, it is a first-class glider. In place of wings it has folds of loose membrane attached to the sides of its body between the fore and hind limbs. When it spreads its limbs, these folds are stretched out tight, making a wonderful gliding surface.

Usually the sugar glider likes to travel from the top of one tree to the base of another. In its glide it may cover a remarkable distance. Launching themselves from the height of a tall tree, some of the larger species may sail almost a hundred yards before they reach the earth.

While gliding, the animal uses its tail as well as the membranes. Its body plays an important role, too, in these airy manoeuvres. The glider twists it at a sharp upward angle just before landing. Thus it checks its speed so it can come to rest in an erect position, ready to scramble upward into the branches without loss of time, perhaps to glide again to the base of another tree.

Strangely enough, not only do these gliders bear a strong resemblance in structure to the true flying squirrels, but their gliding habits are much the same. However, the animals of each group are not related. Each has developed its method of travel on its own.

——Baby Gliders. Baby gliders number one or two in a litter at most. Usually they are born about July. The period of pregnancy, as with all marsupials, is short; about three weeks. The babies grow fast. When they are two months old they are fully clothed in fur and ready to leave the mother's pouch.

At birth, a sugar glider can look forward to a life of from seven to ten years. Few will die of old age, however, for the gliders live surrounded by natural enemies. Chief among them are the owls—in particular those known as the Barking or Winking Owl and the Powerful Owl.

We could hardly call even the largest of the sugar gliders big animals. The several different kinds range in size from seven inches in head-and-body length, with a tail eight inches long, to an overall length of thirty inches. They vary in delicate shades of colour from brownish grey to blackish brown.

The Pygmy Glider, or Feather-tail Glider, *Acrobates*, owes its name to its minute size. It is no more than six inches in length, half of which is tail. It is common in the eucalyptus forests of eastern Australia.

The pygmy glider's habits are rather like those of its big relative, the sugar glider. It is a creature of the darkness. Its soft downy fur muffles all sound so that it travels in silence like a shadow in the night. During the day it hides in hollow branches.

This tiny creature makes a globe-shaped nest of dried leaves and shredded bark. Usually it bears four young, and the mother carries them around in her pouch till they are big enough to take care of themselves.

The Honey Possum or Noolbenger, *Tarsipes*, of south-western Australia, is a beautiful wisp of an animal. It is only seven inches long, four-inch tail and all. Three black stripes run down its grey back; its face, limbs, and feet are a dull reddish brown.

The body of the honey possum is superbly adapted to the kind of life it leads. Indeed, of all the marsupials, this animal is one of the most specialized. Like many of the birds and insects, it is built to get its food from flowers—a long, pointed muzzle and a long tongue enable it to reach into trumpet flowers for nectar and pollen. It will also devour large quantities of honey. Its teeth, small and weak, do not permit it to eat anything more solid than soft-bodied insects.

——IT FOLLOWS THE FLOWERS. Like most other small opossums, this one sleeps all day and comes to life at night. Its whereabouts at any particular time is governed by the flowering plants and trees, some of which are in bloom at all seasons of the year. When the tea tree is in flower it is there—then, later, when the bottle-brushes and gum trees are in bloom, we see it among them.

——QUAINT AND SPRIGHTLY. In its behaviour the honey possum is quaint and sprightly. Its agility is truly remarkable: it is quite at ease hanging upside down by its tail from a slender twig while it noses into a flower on a branch below. Unfortunately, in captivity this amusing little fellow does not survive long.

The female honey possum (she is slightly larger than her mate) bears one to four babies at a time, and has a roomy pouch in which to carry them. The nest is built in the tall grass or tea trees; sometimes a deserted bird's nest does duty as a lodging.

The Koala, *Phascolarctos*, has sometimes been described as the model of our toy teddy bears. Although it looks like the typical bears, it is in no way related to them.

Large and bushy ears, a protruding black nose, and no tail are

A LIVING TEDDY BEAR

The koala is not a bear, nor is it even related to the bear in any way: it merely happens to look like one. Only three feet in length, and weighing up to thirty pounds, this little animal has a charming disposition. Some have said that it provided the original pattern for our common toy bear, but the so-called "teddy bear" was modelled after a grizzly bear cub shown in a cartoon with Theodore Roosevelt in 1902, and was named after that famous conservationist with his consent, we are told.

peculiarities of the koala. Its eyes, small but bright, always exhibit a perplexed expression. This charming little animal seems to be just a living toy—it measures less than three feet in length and weighs up to thirty pounds—designed by nature for a child's delight.

The koala has indeed been copied as a toy, but it was by no means the original model of our toy bears. Various toy bears were on the market in the nineteenth century. The first one known as a "teddy bear" seems to have been made in the first years of the present century. A newspaper cartoon in 1902 depicted Theodore Roosevelt in the role of the protector of a grizzly bear cub, and a toy manufacturer obtained his permission to design a toy bear and call it "Teddy's bear". The name was soon shortened to the one we know so well.

——KOALA BABIES AND PARENTS. A baby koala is a long time a-growing. At birth the koala is not more than an inch long and barely as fat as a lead pencil. Despite its small size, there is never more than one baby in a litter. This only offspring is deposited in the mother's pouch, where little by little it acquires the form we know so well.

At six months the baby is fully furred, has its eyes wide open, and is beginning to take an interest in the outside world. It is now ready to make a daring excursion on its mother's back. A year goes by, and the cub is still a comparatively helpless bundle of fur with sharp black eyes; it clings to its mother's back wherever she goes. In fact, a mother will carry her spoiled youngster until it is nearly as large as herself.

Sometimes, when several females happen to be nursing their children together, the youngsters may become mixed up. No one seems to mind which gets whose milk—a fact that is most unusual among wild as well as domestic animals. After the meal is over, the young return to their rightful mothers. Occasionally one mother will look after her neighbour's baby as well as her own. The father koala, however, shows no interest in family affairs; he is rather annoyed when the baby climbs on his back.

A koala is full-grown when four years old and may live to the ripe old age of twenty. It feeds on the foliage of the eucalyptus tree and the blue gum. In captivity it makes a choice pet but rarely survives very long. Even in the wild a change from one grove of eucalyptus trees to another may prove fatal.

This charming little native of Australia is now found only in limited numbers from Queensland to Victoria.

The Ring-tailed Possum, *Pseudocheirus*, may be as small as a small squirrel, as large as a cat. It has comparatively short fur and a long tail, tapered to the tip, which it can coil around a branch or use as an extra hand. Its thumb and forefinger close to meet the other three fingers— a useful arrangement for a tree-dweller whose life may depend upon the strength of its grip.

Most of all, the ring-tail prefers to make its home in the wet rain forests. Thanks to its wonderful hands and tail, it is extremely graceful in its movements in the trees. It builds a nest like a squirrel and feeds on vegetation.

Like the cuscus, the ring-tail is a night prowler. It has a fixed vacant stare that suggests stupidity, but such a judgment is hardly called for. The stare may be due to the animal's sensitive eyesight, which is adapted especially for the dark. Sight is its guiding sense in the forest at night.

The ring-tailed possum is very quarrelsome with its fellows. But the grievances are not deeply rooted, and the fights are not severe. Usually, the female is the aggressor.

This animal breeds in the first part of the year. Usually two young are born at a time. At birth they are a dark, leaden colour. They are ready to leave the pouch by the end of April, when they look exactly like their parents.

We find several different species of ring-tails in Australia and New Guinea. They vary in colour from light grey to dark reddish brown. The Green Possum, or Striped Ring-tail, has a peculiar greenish tinge to its fur, overlaid with a glistening golden wash, which immediately defines it since green is a unique colour among mammals. It is at home in scrub forests in the mountains of Queensland.

The Great Flying Phalanger, *Schoinobates*, is the largest of the flying possums, being about the size of a house cat. It has set some impressive flight records. In a flying leap it has covered a distance from the top of one 100-foot tree to another 120 yards away.

This big possum is a good climber, too. It utters a peculiar gurgling squeal as it mounts from branch to branch, searching for tender shoots and blossoms of the eucalyptus tree and leaves of the peppermint gum, its rather dainty fare. Its den is a hollow, high up in the trees, which it lines with shredded bark and dead leaves.

Although the pouch of the female great flying phalanger is provided with two nipples, rarely does it have more than one baby at a time. The youngster remains attached to the mother's nipple for six weeks. Soon after, its eyes open and its body gets a downy covering of fur. Four months after birth, the baby is out of the pouch and clinging to the mother's back as she goes about on her nightly excursions for food.

You will come upon these animals in the Australian forests, from Queensland to Victoria. The great flying phalanger is about fifteen inches long and it has a bushy, grasping tail that may reach twenty inches. The fur, ashy grey in colour, is long and soft; the ears are large and naked. Its flying membranes are attached to the elbow—not to the wrist, as in the smaller gliders.

WOMBATS—SKILFUL DIGGERS

The Common or Naked-nosed Wombat, *Phascolomis,* lacks the grace of the possums and phalangers; with its thick chubby body and short legs, it looks and moves about rather like a small bear.

The wombat is a burrower—that is why the Australians often refer

THE TUNNEL-DIGGING WOMBAT
The common or naked-nosed wombat is often called a "badger" in its home, Australia, because it is such a proficient digger. Its burrow has a nest at the end, and is commonly fifteen feet long; however, the wombat can dig one six or seven times as long. Notice the animal's sharp claws and sturdy legs, well suited for tearing open the earth.

to it as a "badger". Its sturdy limbs and stout claws are fine equipment for penetrating the ground. The animal sometimes digs a burrow that extends up to a hundred feet in length, with an underground nest chamber at the end. More usually, however, its burrow is about fifteen feet long.

——ITS TEETH GROW THROUGH LIFE. By day the wombat will hide in its den. When darkness has made the world safe for it, this large, coarse-haired creature emerges to search for food. Strictly a vegetarian, it feeds on grasses, roots, and the inner bark of trees. For such a diet it needs stout teeth. It has them, too—powerful gnawing instruments that continue to grow throughout life, like a rodent's, and just as continually worn down.

The wombat is endowed with a reasonable share of intelligence. It makes a good pet, and readily responds to kindness. In captivity it shows an even disposition. It will eat all kinds of vegetables, and is especially fond of new hay, which it will eat stalk by stalk. A hoarse, growling cough is the loudest sound it produces.

——THE LONG-LIVED WOMBAT. Wombats may live a long time— some tame ones have been known to survive as long as thirty years. They are solitary in their habits, except at mating time. The wombat's breeding season is from the middle of April to the end of June. Usually, the mother raises only one young at a time and carries it around in her pouch in typical marsupial fashion.

——WHERE WE FIND THEM. It is in the coastal regions and the hills of south-eastern Australia—from New South Wales to Queensland, Tasmania, and Flinders Island—that we find the common wombats. The naked-nose variety owes its name to a bare patch on its muzzle. In colour, it varies from almost black to yellowish buff or grizzled. It is practically tail-less, and about forty inches long on an average, but large wombats may be closer to four feet and weigh eighty pounds.

Still, all of these are pygmies compared to their ancestors. Ancient Australia, as we know from the fossil record, had a giant wombat the size of a hippopotamus!

The common wombat is only one of a number of different kinds which make up the family Phascolomidae. Another kind, in contrast, has soft fur and a hairy nose. The thick coarse covering of some has been used to make doormats. The flesh is said to taste like pork.

[1-7]

The female kangaroo carries her lone "joey" in her pouch for about
six months while he grows strong not only in body but in curiosity. When the baby leaves the pouch it will be independent.
See page 60

[1-8]

The hedgehog only looks like a porcupine. While its spines are not barbed like those of the porcupine, they are more than adequate for the little animal's defence. Rolled up with the unprotected head and under-parts tucked inside, it is a formidable ball of sharp bristles.
See page 71

Australian Official Photos

THE WOMBAT OF AUSTRALIA

The wombat looks like a small bear in its coat of long, coarse fur, which may range in colour from buff to almost black. A vegetarian, the wombat uses its lengthy claws mainly for digging. *See page 57.*

THE TASMANIAN DEVIL

The Tasmanian devil has earned the farmer's enmity for killing sheep and poultry. By contrast, most other Australian marsupials are timid and inoffensive. *See page 40.*

Australian Official Photos

KOALA AWAKE

The koala—Australia's "native bear"—is about two feet long and has a prominent snout. This harmless creature spends its life in the trees. It eats leaves, but only certain kinds, and is active principally after dusk. *See page 54.*

KOALA ASLEEP

With its limbs tucked in, the koala naps securely in the trees. Earlier in the century it was almost wiped out for its fur, but today it enjoys government protection.

WALLABIES, PADEMELONS, AND KANGAROOS

Wallabies—Small Kangaroos. In a popular sense the wallabies and pademelons are nothing but rabbit-sized kangaroos. If they were larger they would be called kangaroos, since it is size, in general, that determines which is which. Some wallabies, however, are as large as kangaroos.

Like their big cousins, the wallabies possess excessively large and long hind limbs and feet for hopping and leaping. (*Macropodidae*, the family name which we give to them and the kangaroos, means "great feet".) Their tails are usually long, stout, and powerful; the animals use them more as props and balancing organs than as a means of giving themselves an extra boost when they jump along.

A large number of different kinds of wallabies dwell in Australia, New Guinea, Tasmania, and the neighbouring islands. They are dainty, attractive creatures, often grey or brown in colour, and have harelike habits and great speed. Most of them live on the open plains and do not make a burrow but lie up in "forms"—small depressions in the ground worn down by constant use; others live in the rocks or brush.

Like the rabbits and hares, the wallabies feed on grasses, leaves, and other forms of vegetation. Some species are more or less sociable and live in colonies; others are solitary except during the breeding season. A number come out of hiding only at night, while others are about in broad daylight, although they are not around during the hottest part of the day. Usually, they rear only one offspring at a time.

The Banded Wallaby is the most strikingly marked of all. It has eleven or twelve short stripes running across its grey back from the saddle to the base of the tail. One species, the Nail-tailed Wallaby, is called that because it has a horny projection at the tip of the tail.

The Rock Wallaby is a notable type. Its hind feet are well padded to prevent slipping after a long leap on the well-worn rocks. Like the larger kangaroos, this wallaby loves to bask in the sun, often sitting bolt upright on some rocky point. But it is far from being asleep, and at the first sign of danger disappears in a flash. It performs some astonishingly daring leaps without bringing its forelimbs into use and, when pursued and separated from its rocky castle, will unhesitatingly bound into leaning trees at top speed.

KANGAROOS—SOME LIVE IN TREES

Where They Got Their Name. But for their greater size, the kangaroos are practically the same as the wallabies not only in appearance but in habits as well. They owe their name to Captain James Cook, the famous English explorer of the eighteenth century. In the dialect of the Endeavour River aborigines the word "kangaroo" means "I do not know", and when Captain Cook asked the natives what they called the kangaroo, that is what they are said to have replied; kangaroos the animals have been ever since.

Actually, kangaroos had been heard of by western civilization long before the time of Captain Cook. Captain Francois Pelsaert, wrecked on the treacherous coast of Australia while carrying Dutch immigrants to the Moluccas in 1629, was the first European to make a report on them. The opossums, America's marsupials, were known much earlier.

There are many different kinds of kangaroos. In general they live on the ground, but one has become a creature of the trees. To the world at large, the Great Kangaroo is the most familiar type. Not so well known is the Rat Kangaroo, which is roughly as large as a rabbit but more like a rat in appearance. Some rat kangaroos are hoppers, like the average kangaroo, while others move about rapidly on all fours.

Once the natives hunted the kangaroo extensively for its meat. It is still hunted, but is much harder to find nowadays. Its hide makes an excellent leather for gloves and boots.

The Great Kangaroo, or Forester, *Macropus*, is the largest of all the kangaroos. A male, or "boomer", may stand five to seven feet high and weigh up to two hundred pounds when full grown. The female, or "flyer", is smaller. The great kangaroo dwells in the inland plains of New South Wales and the open forests and brush country of Queensland, south-western Australia, and Tasmania.

The outstanding feature of the great kangaroo is its extremely lengthy, powerful hind limbs, on which the animal hops about. The long, mighty tail serves it as a prop and also gives added impetus to its leaps.

Travelling at a normal rate, the kangaroo jumps from five to ten feet at a time; when pressed for speed, it can cover fifteen or twenty feet in a single bound. According to the nature writer "Mopoke", the record jump was made when a Queensland kangaroo chased by dogs cleared a mass of dead timber ten and one-half feet high; the length of the leap was twenty-seven feet.

——KANGAROO "MOBS". Kangaroos are often encountered in herds or "mobs". In the early pioneer days a "mob" of a thousand head was not unusual, but today it is doubtful if a mob of a hundred could be found. They travel great distances and have no fixed home. Like cattle they lie down and sleep on the ground. As a rule, their diet consists of vegetable matter. Fifteen years is the average life span.

THE GIANT HOPPER

A large and powerful animal, the great kangaroo may weigh up to two hundred pounds and stand five to seven feet high. With the aid of its strong hind legs and thick, massive tail, it can hop along at a speed of twenty-five miles an hour. It is a grazer, and must compete with sheep and cattle for its livelihood.

——BABY KANGAROOS. The young kangaroo or "joey"—rarely, if ever, is more than one reared at a time—is carried in the mother's pouch for the first six months. As the joey develops, it takes more and more interest in the outside world, peering about from its safe retreat while its mother hops along, sometimes at a speed of twenty-five miles per hour when she is in a hurry.

If hard pressed in flight, the female will toss her young into a thicket and lead the pursuers away. Relieved of the extra weight, she may now make good her escape and return later to pick up her joey.

——GENTLE UNLESS PROVOKED. Kangaroos love to take their daily bath in a river, and on occasion they even indulge in sun-bathing. In public parks they will join picnickers and expect to get some of the spoils when lunch is over. They are timid and harmless unless forced to defend themselves. A large male with its back to a tree or wall can protect himself from a whole pack of dogs, and any individual that approaches too close is ripped to shreds by his powerful clawed hind feet.

—— OLD MALES ARE BOLD. Old males have a reputation for boldness. An interesting tale about one of them is related by Carl Lumholtz, in his book *Among Cannibals*:

"A stalwart Highland shepherd was on his way home one evening with his dog, when suddenly he discovered a large object in front of him. Having lately come to Australia, he had scarcely seen one of these animals before, and being very superstitious he thought it was the devil himself. Meanwhile the dog attacked the monster, but instead of taking flight, it assumed the form of a great kangaroo, came up to the shepherd, put its arms around him and hopped away with him. The dog pursued the bold robber until the latter let go of its victim."

——DIFFERENT KINDS OF GREAT KANGAROOS. There are three groups of great kangaroos. The first kind, the Great Grey Kangaroo, or Forester, is found in the open forests and brush country of Queensland and south-western Australia. The second, the Tasmanian Forester, is the only large kangaroo in Tasmania. It is more reddish brown than the mainland grey kangaroo and has coarser and longer fur.

The third, the Red Kangaroo, has a wide range that extends throughout the plains and open forest country of Australia. It is richly coloured, powerful, and one of the most graceful of the large kangaroos. The male is a brilliant wine-red shade. The female, or doe, is more slender than the male, more lightly built, and has great speed. A soft smoky-blue in colour, she has been named the "blue flyer". The red kangaroo is probably the largest and the most gregarious of the kangaroos.

A related form is the Wallaroo or Rock Kangaroo, *Osphranter*. The wallaroo is a large, stocky, powerful kangaroo of the coastal ranges and inland mountains of Australia.

The Tree Kangaroo, *Dendrolagus*, like the other kangaroos, comes from a line of ground-hoppers but has taken to the trees. It still retains the long hind limbs for leaping, but they have become shorter and broader, and the foot pads are rough, to assist in climbing. The animal reaches a length of four feet, about half of which is the tail. The tail is

THE KANGAROO THAT TOOK TO THE TREES

The tree kangaroo is the only one of the kangaroos that has taken up permanent residence in the trees. Though it is still built for hopping, its hind limbs have become shorter, the better for climbing. Using its long tail to help balance and steer itself, this curious animal makes long, flying leaps in the trees.

slender, with a thick brush at the tip, and serves as a rudder in flying leaps in the trees, as well as a balancer.

The tree kangaroo sleeps during the day curled up in the crotch of a tall tree. Frequently several animals occupy the same grove. After sunset they descend to the ground, always backing down tail first, and visit a waterhole for a drink. Their food, in the main, consists of the leaves of the white cedar as well as ferns, creepers, and many kinds of fruits.

Aborigines hunt the tree kangaroos with the aid of trained dingos, the native dogs of Australia, and relish its flesh as food. Usually one of the aborigines goes up the tree to stir the animal up. When it leaps down, the aborigines grab it by the tail or else it is caught by the dogs. A tree kangaroo, when disturbed, will jump down out of a tree from a height of thirty to fifty feet.

Essentially a forest kangaroo, this animal is at home in the mountains and high tablelands of Northern Queensland. There are two species in Australia: Lumholtz's Tree Kangaroo and the Dusky Tree Kangaroo. In New Guinea there are four; they vary in colour from grizzled and white-tailed to greyish brown and golden chestnut with yellow rump and tail.

The Musk Kangaroo, *Hypsiprymnodon*, is the most primitive and the smallest of the kangaroos. It has an overall length of eighteen inches (including a six- or seven-inch tail, which is quite hairless and covered with a scaly skin). Reddish brown in colour, it is a more slender and a prettier creature than the rat kangaroo. It has a peculiar musky odour from which it gets its name.

The habits of the musk kangaroo are much the same as those of the typical kangaroo. Exceedingly shy, it hops around with a rapid motion. It is about in broad daylight and hunts for grubs and insects by turning over debris in the brush. This diet it supplements with tuberous roots, fruits, and berries. Sitting up on its haunches, it will hold a piece of fruit in its forepaws and munch it in a very human fashion.

The musk kangaroo lives in Queensland, where it haunts the damp brush and scrub country bordering lakes and streams. It breeds during the rainy season, which lasts from February to May. The female usually bears two tiny young and carries them around in her pouch.

The Insect-Eaters—Shrews, Moles, Hedgehogs, and Their Relatives

MOST of the shrews, moles, and their kin are little known to us, for they prefer to keep out of man's way. Some live in the trees, a few swim, but the greater number are burrowers; many, like the moles, stay underground practically all the time. They are small or tiny creatures, and, when we do catch a glimpse of them, we may take them for mice or rats.

Enormous appetite, great courage, and pugnacity are typical traits of these little animals. All are highly strung and extremely nervous; sudden fright or shock may even prove fatal to some. They live at high speed, they sleep little, and have a short life.

We find some members of this group in practically every part of the Temperate and Tropical Zones except Australia. Because they feed mostly on insects, they are known as insectivores (order Insectivora). Not all live on such a restricted diet; some eat a wide variety of animal and vegetable food. They have many teeth, extremely sharp and small, and a long snout. They patter along on flat feet armed with claws. Fur or, as in the case of the hedgehog, spines cover their bodies; some wear a coat that is a combination of both.

The insectivores are extremely interesting to us because they are among the most primitive of the mammals. Their brains are decidedly simple, without convolutions, and their teeth are like those we find in the oldest fossil mammals. They even have a collar-bone rather like the shoulder girdle of their reptile ancestors.

NEIGHBOURS OF THE DINOSAUR

These small, shy creatures are actually living relics of the original stock from which our modern, or placental, mammals arose. Over fifty

million years ago, when the earth still trembled to the tread of the
dinosaur, there were already insectivores that looked much like the
common shrews of today. They must have escaped notice then as they
do now; one of them, the long-extinct minishrew, became the great-
grandparent of the whales, elephants, horses, and cattle, the apes, and
man.

Like two other ancient creatures, the opossum and the oyster, the
insectivores have joined the ranks of the immortal. How have they
managed to survive through the ages while many animals that sprang
from the same stock—the woolly mammoth and the sabre-toothed tiger
are good examples—have disappeared from this planet?

The reason seems to be that the insectivores have changed little from
the primitive forms, and always remained obscure. But the specialized
animals grew still more specialized and could not, like the lowly
insectivores, adjust to changing conditions.

SOLENODONS—WEST INDIAN RARITIES

The Solenodon, or Alamiqui, *Solenodon,* looks like a long-snouted
rat. A rare and peculiar creature, it is about the size of a red squirrel
and has rather long, coarse, limp fur, rusty brown in colour. Its head,
exceedingly long, ends in a sharply pointed snout; the nine-inch tail is
naked and scaly. The solenodon's home is the West Indies.

The solenodon is seldom seen outside the exhibition cases of a
museum. This is not surprising, since the animal is extremely scarce
and never comes above ground during daylight hours. It bores under
rotten logs in the jungle floor and beneath loose rocks, searching for
insects, snakes, and burrowing animal life. When pursued, it is said to
practise the so-called "ostrich stunt" of sticking its head in a hole,
leaving its entire body exposed. But we have little accurate information
about its habits.

Two facts are hard at work making this animal rarity still rarer.
First, the solenodon's rate of reproduction is slow, So far as we know,
it produces only one young in a litter. Second, although it has few
natural enemies, it is preyed upon by domestic cats, dogs, and the
recently introduced mongoose, which have all but exterminated it.

——MYSTERY OF THE SOLENODON'S ORIGIN. Where the solenodon
came from—how it came to be part of the impoverished animal life
of the West Indies—is a mystery. It has no relatives on the American

mainland and but few distant ones where it lives. Perhaps it is a survivor from ancient times, when Cuba and Haiti were the highlands of an old continent, now long sunk beneath the waves.

NEAR THE END OF ITS TRAIL

The Haitian solenodon, like its cousin the Cuban solenodon, is rarely seen outside a museum. One reason it is so rare is that it has only one baby in a litter; another is that cats and dogs prey upon it. The little solenodon is close to extinction.

In any event, the solenodons make up a distinct family (Solenodontidae). There are only two species in it: the Cuban Solenodon, with a tawny yellow head; and the Haitian Solenodon, which is darker brown in colour. They are about two feet long from the tip of the snout to the end of the tail.

TENRECS—MADAGASCAR'S SHREWS AND HEDGEHOGS

On the island of Madagascar we find a group of strange insect-eaters known as the tenrecs. Restricted to just this one area, with no close relatives elsewhere, they must inevitably remind us of the isolated solenodons of the West Indies.

The tenrecs and the lemurs are Madagascar's most important native mammals. The island has been separated from the mainland of Africa for long ages, and few other types of animals have had an opportunity to come in. Yet in many ways the little tenrecs make up for their absence. They have specialized, and there are two main kinds, making up the family Tenrecidae: those with soft fur and those with quills. We might consider them to be Madagascar's shrews and hedgehogs, its moles, its mice, and, to a large extent, its rats.

TENRECS WITH SOFT FUR

The Rice Tenrec does the work of a mole. Living underground, it uses its enlarged feet to dig in search of worms and grubs. Its tunnels serve to drain excessive moisture in the ground, and its excavations have improved the fertility of the land. However, it does considerable damage to the rice crops, since it injures the plants' roots as it digs beneath them. It is about the size of a small rat, and has a short tail.

Another kind, the Marsh Tenrec, has broadly webbed feet for swimming; like our water shrews it hunts water-living insects and is roughly the size of a rat. The Pygmy Tenrec, smallest of the Madagascar tenrecs, resembles a tiny long-tailed shrew. It lives in holes in the ground and feeds on small insect life.

More remarkable is the Long-tailed Tenrec. Although the body of this little creature is only about two inches long, it has a five- to six-inch tail. It possesses forty-seven vertebrae (one more than the tree pangolin, formerly supposed to have the greatest number) strung together to form the tail, which is four-sided and angular. Among mammals, only jumpers have tails that are proportionately so long; and since its hind feet are large, the long-tailed tenrec can jump when there is need. In general, it looks like a long-snouted mouse, reddish brown in colour.

SPINY TENRECS

The Common Tenrec, *Tenrec ecaudatus*, is not only the largest tenrec—it is the largest of all the insectivores. This giant of a pygmy order still does not seem very impressive to us: full grown, it measures a mere twelve to sixteen inches. Its head is actually one-third the entire animal. It lacks a tail—"tailless tenrec" is the meaning of its scientific name.

The common tenrec resembles the solenodon a little: it has an elongated face and a long, pointed snout for rooting in the soft earth. Its fur is soft and yellowish brown in colour. When it is quite young the animal sports a coat of brownish spines mixed with coarse hair; as it grows, it loses most of the spines except in the collar around its neck and shoulders. When danger threatens, the spines are erected, presenting a bristling array of protective armour.

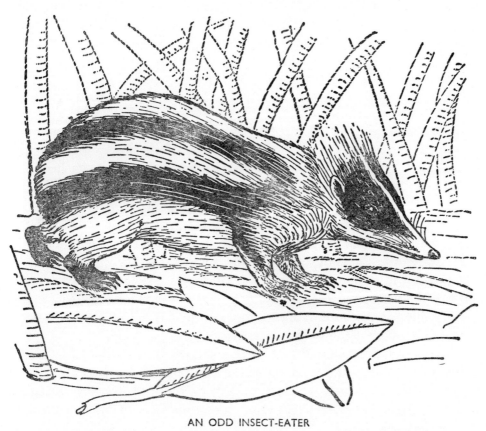

AN ODD INSECT-EATER

Madagascar has a number of curious animals all its own; not the least interesting of them are the tenrecs. Relatives of the shrews, they take the place of the moles, rats, and mice on the island. Shown above is one of the most attractive of the group: the streaked tenrec, a spiny creature with decorative white lines on its yellowish-brown back. It is hardly six inches in length. Tenrecs are among the most primitive of the mammals.

The common tenrec is a mountain-dweller. It lives in holes in the ground and ventures abroad in search of bugs and insects only after nightfall. Although not a sociable creature, it is not exactly solitary either; it has some of the largest families in the mammal world, fifteen to twenty-one young not being unusual. Any mother furnishing milk to so many hungry mouths is kept constantly busy.

From June to December the common tenrec goes to sleep underground for a long, hard-earned rest. At this time the natives dig it out for food.

Other tenrecs look more like the European hedgehog; they are armoured like it, though their spines are not so stout. One of the handsomest is the Streaked Tenrec; it is covered with long, slender spines and has three decorative white lines running along its yellowish-brown back. The animal is only about five inches long and has practically no tail.

POTAMOGALES—STURDY SWIMMERS OF AFRICA

The Potamogale, or Otter Shrew, *Potamogale velox*, of western Equatorial Africa, is the champion swimmer of the insectivores. This streamlined animal looks like an otter: its limbs are short, its head is broad and flattened. Close fur covers its cylindrical body, which joins evenly with the thick neck.

One of the potamogale's most striking features is its powerful, flat-sided tail. It makes up almost half of the animal's two-foot length. This rear emphasis is not wasted by the potamogale. Having no webbed feet to aid it in swimming, it uses the tail instead; swinging it back and forth in the water, the potamogale propels itself along much like a fish. It can achieve a fair rate of speed, too, and that is why scientists call it *Potamogale velox*—"the swift water-weasel".

Fresh water crustaceans, and small fish, are the potamogale's fare. It finds them in the forested watercourses it haunts in its central and West African homeland, which extends from the Cameroons to Angola and the Congo. The potamogales form a distinct family (Potamogalidae) among the insectivores.

GOLDEN MOLES—AFRICA'S UNDERGROUND TORPEDOES

The vast continent of Africa has no true moles like the ones we find in the Northern Hemisphere. But it does have their counterparts in its golden moles. These little underground torpedoes look somewhat like the true moles and behave like them.

The golden moles are burrowers, and the claws on their forefeet are greatly enlarged for digging. They have cylindrical bodies and pointed muzzles, but only a trace of a tail. The fur is full and soft, usually with a brilliant metallic lustre varying from golden bronze to violet.

The Cape Golden Mole, or Goudmoul, is the best known of the family. It has brilliant shades of gold in its fur—no question how it came by its name. One of the smallest of its kind, it is only about four and one-half inches long. Another, the Red Golden Mole, burrows deep in the ground and like the common garden mole pushes up mounds of earth. Still another, the Little Golden Mole, is usually less than four inches long; it travels just below the surface of the ground. Largest of all is the Giant or Forest Golden Mole; it has a length of nine inches and is dark golden brown in colour. It spends most of its time above ground.

The golden moles dwell only in southern Africa. There they range from the Cape of Good Hope north to the Congo, but are absent in the region about Angola and Rhodesia. They make up the family Chrysochloridae—a group that beautifully illustrates nature's habit of developing animals that look like those we encounter elsewhere and even lead the same kind of life, but are nevertheless different.

HEDGEHOGS—THEY ROLL UP INTO SPINY BALLS

The hedgehog is a night prowler. A quill-covered creature less than a foot long, it trots about with a jaunty gait, but its best speed is slow compared with that of its enemies. Fat and tender, it is a choice morsel for any beast of prey.

But acquiring that morsel is the problem. When surprised on its nightly wanderings, the hedgehog makes no attempt to run away unless a shelter is close by. Instead, it rolls itself up in a ball and draws its head and feet together at the inside. Now it is a sphere of bristling spines that defies attack.

BATTLE BETWEEN A HEDGEHOG AND A VIPER

The hedgehog does not use its spines as a weapon. They are strictly a means of defence, though the hedgehog knows how to employ them effectively in getting its food. Just how effectively you will see in this extraordinary report of how a hedgehog tricked an adder into biting itself to death:

"Everyone knows that a hedgehog is a sworn enemy of reptiles in general and of the viper in particular, but few perhaps are aware in what way he contrives to overcome so recalcitrant and dangerous an enemy and make a meal of it.

"My keeper was going his round this summer in a wood which is unfortunately infested with vipers, when he espied an enormous one asleep in the sun. He was on the point of killing it with a charge of shot when he perceived a hedgehog coming cautiously over the moss and noiselessly approaching the reptile. . . .

"As soon as the hedgehog was within reach of his prey, he seized it by the tail with his teeth and quickly rolled himself into a ball. . . . The viper, awakened by the pain, at once turned and made a terrific dart at him . . . infuriated, it extended itself, hissed and twisted

IT ROLLS INTO A BALL

The hedgehog really does roll up into a prickly ball when danger threatens. The animal makes good eating, but the bristling spines baffle attack. Some beasts of prey have found a way to solve the problem—the fox will roll Mr. Hedgehog into a pool of water where he must uncurl or drown. Although the hedgehog's quills resemble those of the porcupine, this is merely a matter of coincidence; the porcupine belongs in another group, the rodents.

with fearful contortions. . . . In five minutes it was covered with blood . . . and lay exhausted on the ground . . . when the hedgehog quietly unrolled himself." (Ferdinand Coste, in the magazine *Zoologist*, 1887.)

The wily fox is perhaps a more formidable enemy for the hedgehog. Foxes are credited with enough forethought to roll the hedgehog into a nearby pool of water, where it will open up and swim rather than drown. Then the fox grabs its prey by the head and the struggle is ended.

FACT AND FICTION ABOUT HEDGEHOGS

Hedgehogs are widespread throughout most of the Old World except Australia and Madagascar. We do not find them anywhere in the New World. Because they are such remarkable little creatures, a curious lore has grown up about them in different countries through the ages. The natives in the province of Hopei, China, for example, will tell you to treat the hedgehog with respect, for it is a sacred animal. In Europe, you will often hear that the hedgehog milks cows but in the wild state hedgehogs do not drink milk, except their mother's, of course. They feed on all manner of creeping things—bugs, cockroaches, beetles, slugs, snails, worms, frogs, rats, mice, and bird eggs, as well as snakes. In fact, they will eat any kind of animal life that they can catch and kill.

They seem equally unexacting about their abode. A cavity in the rocks, a hole in the bank, or a hollow stump will suffice just so long as it is warm and dry. In countries where the winters are cold, the hedgehog hibernates.

THE EUROPEAN HEDGEHOG

In Europe, the best known of the hedgehog family is the Common Hedgehog, *Erinaceus europaeus*. Its homeland extends from England and Ireland all the way east to maritime Siberia, Manchuria, and Korea.

This little animal generally breeds twice a year. About a month after mating time five to seven young are born. The baby hedgehogs spend their early days in a nest of dry leaves and grass that their mother has provided for them in a chamber just below the surface of the ground. They are blind at birth and covered with soft white spines. But in a week the tiny "hogs" can see; the spines are hard at the end of three weeks and coloured like an adult's. In a month the babies are old enough to follow the mother into the outside world.

In spite of their name, hedgehogs are not hogs, but insectivores. Most hedgehogs are chocolate brown in colour, with the tip of the spines yellowish white. The spines are closely packed, and cover the back up to the ears. Coarse hair takes the place of the spines on the face, legs, and under-parts.

Although a hedgehog's spines are sharp enough, they are not barbed like a porcupine's. You can pick the animal up by hand without hurting yourself. It is seven or eight inches long on an average (ten for a large male), with a tail of hardly an inch. From above the hedgehog's body appears egg-shaped; its head is sharp and like a wedge. Males and females look much alike.

Hedgehogs of Other Lands. We find many different kinds of hedgehogs in various parts of the world. Some are only four or five inches long. Closely related are the Gymnures, small rat-like animals, and

AN ANIMAL THAT SMELLS LIKE AN ONION

The common moonrat, a cousin of the hedgehog, lives in Asia. It has an odour, like an onion, that makes its enemies keep their distance. We do not find any members of the hedgehog family outside the Old World.

the Moonrats, of Asia. These hedgehogs are covered with hair instead of spines; one, the Common Moonrat, has a peculiar onion-like smell that is offensive at close range. All are placed in the family Erinaceidae, with the common hedgehog.

A QUNFIDHA OR ARABIAN PORCUPINE

Only a handful of an animal, the qunfidha lives in the desert, where it feeds on insects. Although sometimes known as the "Arabian porcupine", it is not really a porcupine at all, being more closely related to the hedgehog. Hedgehogs are found in many parts of the Old World—in the Mediterranean region, in western Europe, Malaya, India, and Africa. They are insectivores. *See page 71.*

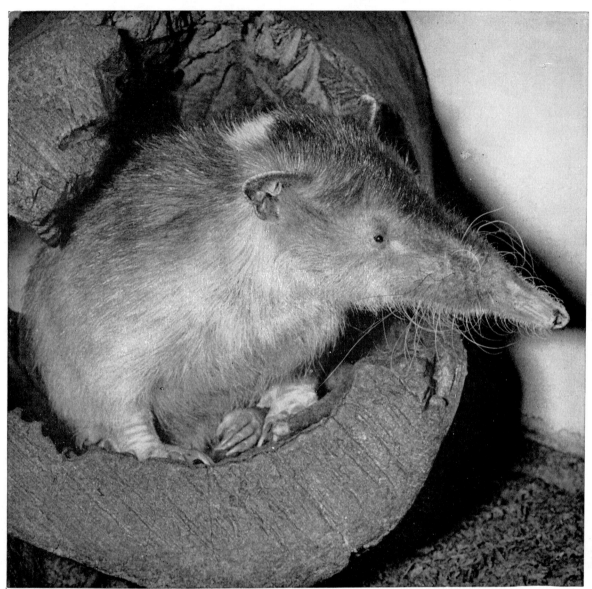

SOLENODON—THE WEST INDIAN RARITY

This peculiar little creature beginning in a long pointed snout and ending in a long pointed tail is seldom seen for two reasons: it is extremely scarce, and spends the daylight hours burrowed under rotten logs in jungle undergrowth, or beneath loose rocks. With no relatives on the American mainland, the solenodon is believed to be a relic of ancient times when the islands were an integral part of the continent. *See page 66.*

Another "look-alike"—the spiny ant-eater of Australia. This shy small animal lays eggs as does the duckbill platypus, and together they represent the world's most primitive mammals.   *See page 24*

[1-9]

[1-9a]

Although they prefer to escape danger by burrowing straight down into the earth, spiny ant-eaters also use their quills in a hedgehog type of defence.
     See page 24

[1-10]

Almost totally blind from a life spent in underground darkness, moles have a difficult time in
their infrequent above-ground foragings.
See page 88

A peculiar star-nosed mole emerges briefly through
the loose dirt of a hillside with the staple of the
mole diet—an earthworm.   *See page 93*

[1-10a]

ELEPHANT SHREWS—SWIFT LITTLE HOPPERS OF AFRICA

The elephant shrew of Africa is one of the oddest animals in a group full of oddities. No bigger than a rat, it has a flexible, sensitive snout that projects stiffly before it. Its chubby, soft-furred body ends in long hind legs; the creature hops around on them like a kangaroo. It has large eyes, unlike most insectivores.

HIGHLY STRUNG RUNNERS AND FIGHTERS

Elephant shrews are sun-worshippers and love to bask, stretched out, in the warm sunshine. Though most active during daylight hours, they are known to be about on moonlit nights. Walking at leisure, the

IT ALMOST SEEMS TO HAVE A TRUNK

The elephant shrew of Africa is a long-snouted creature, often not much bigger than a mouse. It may walk on all fours or hop around on its long hind legs like a kangaroo. The elephant shrew is a highly strung little being, and is often involved in furious fights with its kin. The animal shown above is known as the chequered elephant shrew because of the markings on its back. The life of a shrew is a short one—fifteen months, at most.

elephant shrew may go on all fours. But on the least provocation it leaps away like a little ball of fur, bouncing along, and heads for a retreat in the rocks or the nearest hole in the ground.

While not a typical burrowing animal as judged by its claws, the elephant shrew can quickly dig its way out of sight in reasonably soft soil or sand. Its den may be a crevice in the rocks or a burrow it has

EAL / 1—H

dug in the ground. Besides the usual front door entrance, the elephant shrew's burrow has an emergency exit; it is inconspicuously situated on the surface a few feet from the main entrance, and drops perpendicularly down. If an uninvited guest with a big appetite comes down the main hallway, the shrew scoots away via this escape hatch.

The elephant shrew, like most insect-eating animals, is not a particularly sociable creature: it lives either singly or in pairs. When several are confined in a cage, they box furiously with their hind feet, ripping bunches of hair from the coats of their opponents. As they fight, their ears and whiskers vibrate constantly.

Baby elephant shrews are born one or two in a litter. At birth they are fairly big compared with their mother, and well clothed with fur. Their eyes are already open, or will be very soon. Mother elephant shrew is attentive to her babies' welfare. For example, a female was taken carrying her twin young around attached to her teats. Upon release she made sure that the babies had a firm hold before she bounded away.

There are many kinds of elephant shrews in Africa, from the Cape to Algeria. They occupy almost all types of country; these animals are at home in the deserts of the Sahara as well as the forested regions of the Congo. Most species in the group (family Macroscelididae) are small, with a body about four or five inches long and a tail of the same length. The largest is the Chequered Elephant Shrew, a forest-loving species of the Congo and Kenya. Its body is about eleven inches long, and it has a nine-inch tail. Its back is marked like a chessboard, with four or five rows of evenly spaced light and dark square spots.

TRUE SHREWS—SMALLEST MAMMALS IN THE WORLD

The smallest mammals in the word belong to the shrew family. Most shrews are tiny—the largest is scarcely as big as a house rat. Relatives of the moles, they are mouselike animals with a long, pointed head, minute eyes, and short, rounded ears that are almost concealed in the soft fur.

Shrews live just below the surface of the ground. Their favourite food is insects, and they play an important part in the control of the injurious species, especially before the larvae develop and leave the ground. Shrews also hunt their food under fallen leaves and rotting vegetation. They feed almost continuously, and can consume their own weight in food every three hours. Constantly on the move, these highly strung creatures are active in all seasons, by day and by night.

Two or three times a year, the shrew breeds. Young born in the early spring will scarcely last the year out, but those born in the later summer, barring accidents, live through to the following year. The rate of reproduction varies in different places. In one place, shrews may outnumber all other species of animals and fairly swarm over the land; just a few miles away there may be scarcely any shrews.

THE WELL-ARMED SHREW

Shrews have lots of enemies. Hawks, owls, snakes, weasels, cats, foxes, and fish will kill a shrew on sight. But few will eat it, and for a very good reason: the shrew has a pair of glands, one on each flank, that secrete an objectionable, strong musky odour. An animal with a sense of smell finds it hard to tolerate.

Many people that have never before seen a shrew, experience an eerie feeling when one comes along for the first time. There is a widespread belief that the bite of the shrew is poisonous. The more intelligent pooh-pooh the idea; they even let shrews bite them and suffer no ill effects. The fact is that most shrews have poisonous salivary glands in the lower jaw, but the poison is capable only of a slightly crippling effect on a small mouse. There is one exception—the bite of the American short-tailed shrew may actually kill a mouse.

The feature that distinguishes the shrews from all other animals is their front teeth. Those of the upper jaw are hooked and have a supplementary prong. The lower front teeth are long and project straight forward. These creatures are often classified by the colour of their teeth or the length of their tails. Thus there are red-toothed shrews and white-toothed shrews, long-tailed shrews and short-tailed shrews. Some, known as water shrews, are capable swimmers. They form a great family, the Soricidae; here we can look at only a few of its most interesting members.

SOME INTERESTING RED-TOOTHED SHREWS

The Long-tailed or Red-toothed Shrew, *Sorex,* is found in incredible numbers and varieties in many parts of the Northern Hemisphere—

in the Old World as well as in the New. Besides the lengthy tail that gives it its name, the animal has a long head with almost sightless eyes and a sharply pointed muzzle. The body is small and covered with thick, soft, blackish-brown fur. Its limbs are short. The name "red-toothed", sometimes applied to it, refers to the tips of its teeth, which are heavily coated with deep brownish-red pigment.

The long-tailed shrew is one of the most active mammals alive today. It is almost always astir—in neither light nor dark, summer nor winter, does it slow down. It feeds almost constantly; if deprived of food even for two or three hours it will die of starvation.

Although some species weigh no more than a few grammes, they can withstand temperatures of from 75 to 85 degrees below zero Fahrenheit. The Pygmy Long-tailed Shrew, *Microsorex*, weighing about two and one-half grammes, is the smallest animal in America. Another little shrew, the Least Long-tailed Shrew, *Sorex minutus*, is one and one-half inches long, with a tail slightly shorter. It is the smallest shrew found in Great Britain, with a range extending across into Asia.

Long-tailed shrews, like other shrews, are very aggressive and, when not feeding they are fighting each other. There are few without some battle scars. A shrew can live peaceably only with its mate; it even shows devotion during the breeding season. Occasionally five or six shrews are found together in one nest; but they are all of one family, not yet broken up.

The American Water Shrew, *Sorex palustris*, an excellent swimmer, is one of the most interesting animals in North America. At first glance it looks like a miniature muskrat without eyes and ears (they are so minute), but the face is more pointed.

This little creature is large in comparison with other shrews: its head-and-body length will reach three inches, and the tail is almost as long again. The tail is compressed at the sides. Swinging it back and forth, the shrew is able to achieve considerable power and shoot rapidly forward in the water. Its hind feet are especially long and conspicuously fringed with stiff hairs for swimming. Its thick black, velvety fur is so dense that it keeps the animal's body dry in the water.

——IT WALKS ON WATER! We have said that the water shrew is an excellent swimmer. For its size, it compares favourably with our fastest freshwater swimmers, such as the otters. It can dive, float, or run along the bottom of shallow pools; and, believe it or not, this dainty little animal can actually walk and run on the water without breaking through the surface film! The feet hold globules of air as it skims across a quiet pool.

Water-walking unfortunately has its drawbacks. Skimming along the surface, the water shrew is an easy prey for the swift-swimming trout or pickerel.

This animal seems less quarrelsome than most shrews and may even be sociable. Several often live together in a hollow tree stump over-hanging a stream. Once a year, the water shrew raises a family of six.

The water shrew frequents watercourses, usually at a moderate elevation, in the northern United States and Canada. It is more active by night than most shrews, and feeds on water spiders, freshwater crustaceans, and tiny fish.

The Cinereous Shrew, or Masked Shrew, *Sorex cinereus*, is the commonest of the shrews in the northern United States and Canada. It is a tiny creature, yet so ferocious that if two are placed together in a small container, one will slay and devour the other in the space of a few hours.

——A WISP OF AN ANIMAL. Even in adulthood the cinereous shrew is just a wisp of an animal. It weighs no more than three and one-half grammes (the weight of approximately one teaspoonful of water); newborn, it is one-tenth of a gramme. The animal is brown above, greyish below. Its life is spent in the dark shadows, under leaves, and in subsoil runways. And so, despite its abundance, it is rarely seen.

A leaf or grass nest in a hollow log, under a stump, or in a hole just below the surface of the ground, is the house where the young shrews are born. Often the nursery consists of a ball-shaped bundle of grass, about eight inches across, with a three-inch chamber in the centre; the entrance is a small hole in the side.

——BABIES AS SMALL AS HONEYBEES. Mother shrew bears six babies as a rule, but she may have as many as ten. At birth, they are naked, with wrinkled pink skin, and are about the size of a honeybee. The mother must be endlessly active in order to satisfy her own hunger as well as to maintain the milk supply needed by her growing family. At one week the tiny tots are beginning to get some fur. A week later, they are fully clothed; during the third week they cut their first teeth and their eyes are open.

When a month old, the tots are weaned; they are now adults and must go out into the world to make a home for themselves. In place of mother's milk the adolescent shrew gulps down crickets, grasshoppers, slugs, and larvae of flies, moths, and earthworms; shrews destroy hordes of injurious insects.

A shrew has its playful moments and will toy around with a beetle just as a cat will play with a mouse.

——1,380 HEARTBEATS A MINUTE. The cinereous shrew is perhaps the most sensitive, highly strung, and nervous of all mammals. When it becomes excited, its heart can speed up to 1,380 beats a minute, a fabulous rate. (Compare that to the normal human heartbeats of sixty-five to ninety per minute!) The animal nearly always dies within a few minutes of capture—even when caught in a trap with a door padded to deaden the sound and shock.

——THE ESKIMO AND THE SHREW. Nervous though the shrew is, we have seen that many people around the globe view it with dread. The Eskimos, in particular, treat it with great caution. They believe that if the animal is disturbed, it will dart at the intruder, burrow through his flesh, enter his heart, and kill him. Meeting a shrew, an Eskimo will stand still as a stone until it has passed by, and thank his lucky stars that he has escaped unharmed.

Life expectancy for the cinereous shrew is about fourteen months —a rather good span considering the host of enemies a tiny creature like this must face.

The Common Red-toothed or European Shrew, or Shrew Mouse, *Sorex araneus,* is a little animal that dwells in great numbers in England, western Europe, and east across Asia. Its body is dark brown in colour, and may measure up to two and one-half inches; the tail, an inch shorter. For its size, this creature has played an enormous role in European folklore.

Like other shrews, the common red-toothed shrew is very pugnacious. Five or six at a time have been observed squeaking and quarrelling among themselves for no apparent reason; in an instant two or three will be at one another's throats, biting and rolling over in confusion. Then one darts off with the others in fast pursuit, and when they catch up with it the rough-housing starts again.

——BABIES IN A BALL OF GRASS. This shrew begins to breed in April. When the mating season opens there is a constant battle among the males, and they utter shrill cries as they fight their fast and furious duels. The breeding season lasts until November.

Mother shrew bears three or four broods a year, with from five to eight young in each. They are tiny, naked, pink little atoms at first, but grow very rapidly. The nursery is a neatly woven ball of grass or leaves placed in a wood-pile or a tuft of grass. It has interlocking blades of growing grass woven into the dome, and is well-roofed to shed moisture; there is an entrance at the side. The young stay at home until nearly fully grown.

——A HIGH DEATH RATE. European shrews are often found dead without a mark on them. The rate of mortality is very high for various reasons.

Shrews often die of starvation; some are drowned by heavy rain; many die of shock during thunderstorms. All flesh-eaters prey on the shrew—hawks, owls, jays, crows, weasels, foxes, cats.

——THE "DANGEROUS" SHREW. European folklore had it—and perhaps still has it, in some places—that a shrew would die if it crossed the path of a human being. It was considered dangerous to livestock. The superstitious believed that whenever a shrew scurried over a horse, cow, or sheep, it would cause the animal extreme anguish and even the loss of any limb the shrew touched.

As protection against this accident, Europeans of the past kept a shrew-ash. They made it by boring a hole in the trunk of an ash tree; an unfortunate live shrew was thrust in the hole, which was then securely plugged up. They believed that touching the shrew's victim with a twig from this tree immediately relieved the pain. The ceremony was accompanied by incantations long since forgotten.

Perhaps because the shrew was considered so obnoxious—or possibly because it is such a fighter—the English-speaking peoples have borrowed its name to describe a turbulent or brawling woman.

Shrews were held sacred by the ancient Egyptians; they supposed the animals were blind and regarded them as an emblem of primal night and darkness. The city of Buto, said Herodotus, was a place of sacred sepulture for these little animals, and mummified shrews have been found in Thebes.

The Old World Water Shrew, *Neomys*, is a handsome little native of England, the mainland of Europe, and northern Asia. Although mostly blackish brown in colour, it has silvery-white under-parts. Its head-and-body length is about two and one-half to three inches or more, its tail about as long again.

The Old World water shrew has habits much the same as the American water shrew's. A frequenter of small streams and marshes, it is a first-class swimmer. Often, however, it is found at considerable distances from water; in England it is as common along the hedgerows as in the streams. It makes its nest in a hole in the bank, lining it with leaves and dried grass. Here the female raises the four to eight young she produces in one litter.

This shrew feeds on water insects and crustaceans. It can be easily and safely caught by hand under the banks of shallow brooks; in captivity it will kill and eat prey as large as frogs.

——THE WATER SHREW IN ACTION. Dovaston, at the beginning of the last century, was one of the first English naturalists to take particular notice of this beautiful little creature. Here are some of the water shrew's habits as he observed them:

"It dived and swam with great agility and freedom, repeatedly gliding from the bank under water, and disappearing under the mass of leaves at the bottom, doubtless in search of insect-food. It very shortly returned and entered the bank, occasionally putting its long, sharp nose out of the water and paddling close to the edge. . . . Sometimes it would run a little on the surface, and sometimes timidly and hastily come ashore, but with the greatest caution, and instantly plunge in again."

SOME NOTABLE SHORT-TAILED SHREWS

The American Short-tailed Shrew, *Blarina brevicauda,* is an animal of special value to the farmer, since it kills insect and rodent pests. It has a short, thickset body, covered with soft, bluish-black fur, and weighs up to thirty grammes (approximately one ounce). With its bobtail, it has a length of about four inches. Its teeth are pigmented with a deep red stain.

This short-tailed shrew is common in the eastern United States; it ranges from south-eastern Canada south to Florida, and west to Manitoba and Oklahoma. It lives in fields or under dead leaves on the forest floor. Not only does it feed on the larvae and worms it finds here, but it also follows subterranean passages in search of insects and mice. Driven by an insatiable appetite, it will kill and devour a mouse its own size.

——A "Poisonous" Animal. The poison of the short-tailed shrew is very similar to that of a cobra. A large dose of saliva, drawn from the glands in its lower jaw and injected into a mouse, will bring about convulsions and death from failure to breathe. Still, human beings do not have to fear these little killers. The writer has caught many of them by hand and suffered no ill effects from their bites.

This animal makes its home underground in a small hole, which it lines with grass. It breeds three or four times a year. The mother may bear as many as nine babies in a litter, but six is the average number.

A SHREW WITH A COBRA'S POISON

The American short-tailed shrew is the farmer's friend. It is death to insects and rodents, for its salivary glands contain a poison similar to a cobra's. This can quickly subdue a mouse but does little hurt to human beings. Tail and all, this venomous little creature is only some four inches long. It is active by day, but generally stays out of sight.

——Little Shrews with Gigantic Appetites. We find a related shrew in Asia, the Oriental Short-tailed Shrew. The smallest of its kind in the Western Hemisphere is the Pygmy Short-tailed Shrew, with an over-all length of about three inches. It is found from Connecticut south through Mexico and Central America into South America; indeed, it is the only type of shrew we find in South America.

The following anecdote from the author's own experience with a captive Connecticut specimen (not over four grammes in weight) well serves to illustrate the voraciousness of the group:

On one occasion a large can of earthworms had been left in the animal's cage. The shrew climbed into the can, dragged out a worm, and slaughtered it after a skilful exhibition of avoiding the writhing coils. Then the bloody assault continued until every worm was completely mangled. Whereupon, after having carefully examined the can to see if any prey was still alive, the shrew proceeded to gorge itself on the torn remains.

WHITE-TOOTHED SHREWS—INCLUDING A "HERO"

The White-toothed Shrew, or Musk Shrew, *Crocidura*, is the common shrew of the Old World and the tropics; we do not find it in America. Most of its kind are a uniform light grey or brown, but some are dark brown. They emit a powerful odour, as their common name tells us.

The African Musk Shrew is perhaps the most unpleasant, evil-smelling, and vicious of the insectivores. It will dare to attack animals much larger than itself, including snakes and small mammals. Its awful stench protects it from the attack of flesh-eating mammals and birds alike.

——A CRUEL CUSTOM. The natives place these shrews in tiny cages and sell them for a penny apiece. The purchaser who puts two in one cage with some scraps of meat will witness a mortal combat. Screaming over the scraps, the shrews proceed to tear each other to bits. The victor not only devours the booty but the vanquished foe as well.

Such frightful carnage may seem unwarranted, but not to the natives of tropical countries, where vermin multiply so rapidly that even the most vigorous measures hardly serve to hold them in check.

——STENCH INTO PERFUME. By some simple but secret method, the natives of West Africa convert the evil stench of this shrew into a delicate, fragrant perfume; it has a sweet smell something like that of sandalwood. In the process the shrew is boiled whole along with certain leaves and palm oil.

The musk shrew is spread over Asia and most of Africa, with several types in Europe. In the British Isles it is found in the Scilly Islands. It measures about two or three inches, with a tail almost as long, but some African species are the size of a rat. The fur is never quite so dense as in the northern shrews, and there is usually a sprinkling of extra-long hairs on the tail.

The Indian House Shrew or Musk Shrew, *Suncus coeruleus*, in its native India and Ceylon, is almost as closely associated with human dwellings as our house rats and mice. It is none other than Kipling's Chuchundra, referred to in his famous story "Rikki-tikki-tavi" as the creature that always creeps by the walls and never comes out in the middle of the floor.

——"MONEY MOUSE." This shrew is a big fellow: it is some six inches long, plus a tail half that length. In semi-darkness the animal's light bluish-grey colour produces a peculiar, almost luminous, effect. When running, it has a queer habit of making a noise like the jingle of silver coins; the natives call it the "money mouse".

Although the house shrew has typically poor eyesight, this weakness has not prevented it from acquiring an outstanding record as a destroyer of cockroaches and other house vermin. It can be taught to come when called, and with a little coaxing will soon take cockroaches and other insects offered by hand. It will immediately kill a large rat placed in the same cage with it.

You might suppose that the house shrew would be especially welcome in tropical areas, where there are periodic outbreaks of rodent-borne plagues. Unfortunately it is killed on sight by natives. Yet it is inoffensive to man, except for its rather musky odour. Tradition has it that this shrew will contaminate with its smell anything it crosses, even a sealed bottle of wine.

——SMALLEST MAMMAL ON EARTH. The house shrews are found in many parts of eastern and southern Asia and also in southern Europe. Most of them are rather small; the Etruscan Shrew, of the Mediterranean region of southern Europe, is the smallest mammal in the world. Its head and body measure only one and one-half inches, and its tail is about one and one-eighth. It is half an inch shorter in body length than America's smallest shrew and weighs less than two grammes.

The Hero Shrew, or Armoured Shrew, *Scutisorex*, has been heard of far outside its native Congo and Uganda. It owes its fame to an unusually strong, reinforced backbone. The animal is large for a shrew, with a head-and-body length of almost six inches and a tail three inches long. It has thick fur, dull brownish black in colour.

——CONGO NATIVES SHOW OFF ITS STRENGTH. The Mangbetu natives of the Congo, whenever they get a chance, take delight in showing before a fascinated crowd the extraordinary resistance of this shrew to weight and pressure. Usually after a hubbub of invocations a man—he may weigh about 160 pounds—steps barefooted upon the shrew, and balances himself on it on one foot. He continues his eloquence for several minutes in this position.

Upon release, the shrew, after a few shivering movements, continues on its way none the worse for the mad experiment. Any other shrew or small rodent submitted to such treatment would be instantly killed.

——A MIGHTY BACKBONE. What makes this animal so strong? The backbone of the hero shrew is strikingly different from that of other shrews. It has more than twice as many vertebrae as they, and these bones are enormously enlarged and staunchly interlocked. The great strength of the backbone together with a strong curve of the skeleton behind the shoulders protects the heart and other vital organs from being crushed. These physical traits may be of value in shielding the animal when it crawls under loose rocks in search of insects and grubs.

——MAGICAL POWERS. It was the Mangbetu natives who originally named this creature a "hero". They believe that the hero shrew's charred body, when prepared by their medicine men, transmits heroic qualities. Accordingly, they wear it as a talisman or take it as medicine. Those engaging in warfare or setting out upon an equally dangerous mission, such as hunting elephants, are eager to carry along the hero shrew's ashes.

SHREW MOLES, DESMANS, AND TRUE MOLES

All the true moles and their relatives, the desmans and shrew moles, make their home in the Northern Hemisphere—we do not meet them in Africa and Central or South America. They are fairly small animals, with a long, pointed head, soft thick fur, tiny eyes and ears, and rather large forefeet. They feed mainly on insects and worms. Most live underground.

Of these animals, the moles, with their powerful claws and fore-limbs, have made the best adaptation to a life of digging beneath the surface. The shrew moles, in their physical traits, are in between the moles and the shrews. For example, the American Shrew Mole, or Gibbs' Mole, as it is also known, has the long face of a shrew, but its muzzle is naked like a mole's. Its forefeet are larger than a shrew's and stoutly clawed, but they have not quite reached the extreme development we find in the broad front feet of the true mole.

Although, like the mole, the shrew mole tunnels in search of worms and burrowing insects, it spends a good part of its life on the surface, a habit it shares with the shrew. The American shrew mole inhabits a narrow strip along the Pacific coast of North America. Across the ocean, in Japan, lives its cousin the Japanese Eared Shrew Mole. This little animal is unusual in that it has a distinct external ear.

The desmans are the aquatic members of the mole family (Talpidae). However, they too make their homes underground.

THE DESMANS—SLOW SWIMMERS IN WEARY RIVERS

The Russian Water Mole or Desman, *Desmana,* is not a true mole, although it resembles one in a general way. It has thick, close, blackish-brown fur (like a mole's), but this is overlaid with long oily guard hairs to shed water. One of its outstanding features is its long, tubular muzzle, which extends far beyond the margin of the lower lip, forming a proboscis. Its hind feet are broadly webbed, and it has a long, scaly tail—almost half the animal's over-all length of sixteen inches or so. The tail is flat on the sides, like the blade of an oar, and forms a powerful instrument for propelling the animal through the water.

——SURVIVOR OF A BYGONE AGE. Though possessing many of the qualifications for an aquatic life, the desman is not very quick in the water. Its inferiority in this respect is due to its descent from ancestral mole stock. The molelike body of this survivor of a bygone age just has not changed enough to permit it to make the most of a life in the water. Thus it favours slow-moving streams or still lakes. As it swims, only the tip of its long, flexible snout is out of the water; the snout is constantly in motion when the animal is on the move.

The desman feeds on leeches, frogs, freshwater crustaceans, molluscs, insects, and fish. It prods in the mud with its proboscis, searching for animal life, and can strike a fair blow with it. It will kill and eat a large carp.

Early spring is the desman's breeding season. The young are born about May, and number from two to six. A second litter may come later in the year. The desman is a rather sociable creature, and seven or eight fully grown individuals have been found in one den.

——THE DESMAN'S HOME. It is in the bank of the same sluggish stream or river it swims in that we can look for the home of the desman. In a spot reinforced by the interlocking roots of trees and shrubs, the animal begins to dig in the bank at water level. A foot or more from the entrance, it excavates upward, hollowing out the nest chamber close to the surface; it pushes the excess earth up through the roof, which produces a raised dome. From the entrance the desman keeps canals open through the muddy shallows for a safe journey to deep water.

The home is a more or less permanent abode. A strong odour surrounds it, arising from the rotting bones of fish dragged into the nest. Here the desman stays when it is not hunting; usually seen about the time of the ice break-up in the spring, when high waters flood it out of its den.

The Russian desman is a native of northern Europe and Russia. A related animal, the Spanish Desman, has a smaller body and a rounder tail, but its habits are much the same.

TRUE MOLES—REMARKABLE DIGGERS

Most people think that they know what a mole is, but few have ever seen one, and these would probably not recognize it if they did. What does this remarkable animal actually look like?

The mole is virtually an underground bullet. It is cylindrical in shape and tapered to a point at the front end. It has no visible neck. Its limbs are short; the forelegs, highly specialized for digging, are broad and tremendously powerful. They are armed with stout claws, with which the mole is capable of excavating a hundred-yard tunnel in twenty-four hours. Six inches (including a one-inch tail) is about the average length of this hard-working creature.

The true moles live in the northern temperate regions of both the Old World and the New World. They do not penetrate into the extreme north because there the ground freezes to too great a depth. They have not invaded the tropics because the soil is, for the most part, too dry to support sufficient underground animal life to compensate for the labour of excavating.

Moles, like other forms of wild life, must get a "living wage". As they dig, they must secure enough food to produce again the amount of energy they expend. Each day they eat their own weight in insects. No other mammals put in so many hours of hard manual labour as the lowly moles.

How the Mole Serves Man. Although the mole raises unsightly mounds of earth on lawns and in pastures, and is often accounted a general nuisance, it plays an important part in developing the soil and keeping it suitable for farming.

In low-lying plains, where too much water would normally turn the soil sour, mole runways drain off the excess. In dry pastures the runways convey the rain underground and distribute it where it is needed most, before it can run off over the hard parched surface.

Then, too, by transferring the subsurface soil to the top, the moles till the land, mixing it with dead leaves or rotting vegetation. In this way they help to produce the rich loam man needs to raise fine crops.

Life Under the Ground. Moles never leave any outside door open to their labyrinth of subterranean highways. From time to time a pile of excavated earth is pushed up through a hole, but once the job is done the exit is firmly plugged. They probably have some sort of community life, since they have passageways in common; where the traffic is too heavy there may be "one-way streets", too. These animals are as pugnacious as shrews, and two moles confined in a small space, will fight until one is killed. They give no quarter and apparently expect none.

Danger in the Daylight. In the course of their underground existence, moles have almost completely lost their sight; at best they can only distinguish between day and night. Rarely do they emerge from their tunnels. In the spring, for example, the garden mole comes out to collect leaves and dry grass for a nest in which to raise its young. Overhead, soaring hawks are on the watch for the poor blind mole, which is not aware of its danger until too late.

Once the nest-building period is over, the mole is reasonably safe for another year. Under the ground, its exquisitely sensitive snout is more helpful than the sharpest of eyes.

Valuable Fur. Moles have one of the finest grades of fur. In the wholesale fur market, dealers' quotations are in the hundreds of thousands of pelts, but it is only in Europe that moles are sufficiently abundant to produce such quantities for the trade.

There are many different kinds of true moles, showing interesting variations from the general stock. In Japan there is the Furry-snouted Mole, a smaller-than-average species, that has a very long, pointed snout covered with short, velvety fur like the body. In southern Asia, the Club-tailed Mole has a tail enlarged at the tip; the Spindle-tailed Mole, of Burma and Yunnan, gets its name from its unusually thick tail.

EUROPE'S COMMON MOLE

The Common European Mole or Oont, *Talpa europaea,* inhabits the temperate regions of the Old World, from England and France to Japan. Five and one-half inches long, with a naked tail of about one inch, it has uniform black velvety fur, sometimes with a greyish or brownish tinge. Occasionally, there is an albino or piebald mole, but more often the off-coloured ones are buff or steel-grey.

The European mole's normal life is spent underground. Twice a year, once in the spring and again in the autumn, it deliberately breaks the surface and ventures out in the open air. In the spring it is for bedding to make a nest. In the autumn, when the ground is hard and dry from the summer heat, the animal must go in search of water.

Interestingly enough, this subterranean dweller is a good swimmer. Occasionally it crosses rivers, and it has been seen swimming strongly in a lake one hundred yards from shore. But such excursions are unusual.

——UNDERGROUND SPEEDSTERS. The European mole is sociable to a degree. In a given area the moles dig main community highways. These thoroughfares, about a foot below the surface of the ground, are connecting arteries between the favourite hunting grounds. They may be used by forty or more moles.

In their underground tunnels these animals are credited with a speed of two and one-half miles an hour. They are as much at ease in the earth as the fish is in the sea.

——MATING OF THE MOLES. The mating season begins in March and lasts until May. The moles fight fierce battles for possession of the females. The female, either with or without the assistance of her mate, builds a regular fortress for her family far off the beaten track.

[1-11]

A prodigious labourer, equipped with powerful claws, the mole can tunnel one hundred yards in twenty-four hours.   *See page 88*

Cross-section of a molehill. The mole's maze of passageways will intersect those of his neighbours, but no "outside door" is ever left open. *See page 88*

[1-11a]

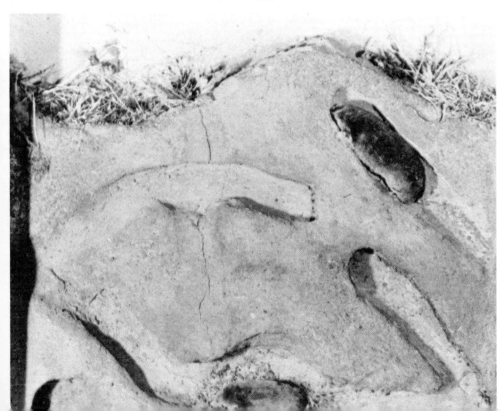

No bigger than a one-inch bit of lead pencil at birth, the koala matures very slowly. Its doting mother will lug it with her for a year or more, until it is almost as big as she is. *See page 54*

[1-12]

[1-12a]

The short-tailed shrew, like other members of the family, is constantly on the move. Feeding almost continuously, they can eat their own weight in food every three hours. *See page 82*

Bats are usually either migratory, or hibernate. The adaptable silver hair, one of the few North American migrators, will hibernate if caught by a sudden onset of cold weather.   *See page 121*

[1-13]

NATIONAL AUDUBON SOCIETY

[1-13a]

Bats sleep upside down. While the majority seek substantial shelter, those who do sleep in the open can fold their wings about them for protection against the elements.   *See page 98*

[1-14]

The bat is the only mammal with real wings—greatly modified forearms and "hands" covered with an elastic membrane that extends all the way down to the feet.
See page 98

NATIONAL AUDUBON SOCIETY

[1-14a]

Dewdrops form on a pygmy. Bats range in size from a five-foot wingspread to these tiny creatures no bigger than a humming-bird.   *See page 122*

This fortress is a molehill, larger than usual and raised above possible high-water level in marshy areas.

In the molehill, at about ground level, or higher, the female hollows out a cavity one foot through, for the nest chamber. Here she weaves an elaborate, compact nest, like a ball, from leaves and grass. She provides an emergency exit at the bottom of the nest chamber, which she often surrounds with an intricate labyrinth. The actual entrance is from below. There is no regular opening to the surface, though the hungry weasel would no doubt welcome one.

Four weeks after mating the female gives birth to a family of from two to six. At first the young are quite naked and helpless, with wrinkled little pink bodies. But they grow very rapidly; at five weeks they are ready to leave the nest and show what good diggers they are. A second litter may come in the autumn.

——THE MOLE IN FOLKLORE. There are many quaint notions about the European mole. Superstition would have it, for example, that the mole possesses only one drop of blood. According to folklore, too, the mole leaves the ground once a year to take a little fresh air in the daylight. In reality, the mole finds its air in the earth; thirst is more likely to bring it to the surface, as we have seen.

MOLES OF NORTH AMERICA

The Common American Garden Moles, *Scapanus* and *Scalopus,* each have their own particular territory in the United States. The Western Garden Mole, *Scapanus,* lives only in the region west of the Rocky Mountains. The Eastern Garden Mole, *Scalopus,* is found from Massachusetts to Nebraska, and as far south as the Gulf of Mexico.

Superficially these animals look alike, with their thick, close coats, almost black in colour, but the western mole is the larger of the two. Indeed, with its seven- to nine-inch length it is the largest mole in America. (The eastern mole measures seven inches.)

The common mole prefers open country for its activities: it favours low-lying meadows and lawns, where the soil is soft and moist, but it may live on hillsides. In these places it digs its two sets of tunnels— one a deep set and the other near the surface.

The creature's deeper runway is from one to two feet under the ground; here the mole spends the greater part of its time and has its living quarters. The surface runway is where the mole finds most of its food. It is used only occasionally, and sometimes only once—when the food supply is gone, the mole digs onward and elsewhere. Some of the passageways extend half a mile or more.

——The Master Tunnellers. The mole is a superb digger. It feels its way with its sensitive snout, then drives its shovel-like feet into the earth and scoops the soil, one handful at a time, to the rear. By pressing its body first against one side, then against the other, it makes the walls compact.

A REMARKABLE DIGGER

There are two common American garden moles—the Eastern Garden Mole and the Western, which is shown above. Both are talented diggers and can hollow a tunnel out at the rate of fifteen feet an hour. The animals' underground activities have great value in keeping the soil fertile. Commonly, nothing is seen of the moles except their molehills; however, moles may be glimpsed above ground in the spring, which is their mating season.

When sufficient soil has been excavated, the mole turns around and pushes the load up through a hole in the roof, forming a heap or "molehill". For the observer, these heaps, piled at intervals on the surface, mark the course of the mole's upper runway.

The animal has a sense of direction for its tunnels. Under hollows and over ridges it keeps approximately the same depth. It can excavate tunnels, shovelling away the dirt, at a rate of up to fifteen feet an hour.

——THE WAY OF A MOLE WITH A WORM. Earthworms are the principal food of the American garden moles, but they will eat almost any kind of insects or larvae they find in the runways. The western mole will eke out its diet with roots or tubers and may eat tulips and iris bulbs. Such depredation cannot be charged against the eastern mole.

The way of a mole with a worm is an interesting one. The mole first grabs the victim, then works along until it comes to one end, usually the head; it commences to devour it like spaghetti, straightening out the kinks in the worm with its forefeet and at the same time scraping off the loose earth.

——FAMILY LIFE AMONG THE MOLES. The common mole makes its nursery in a lower-level tunnel. The chamber is about eight inches in diameter, and the female lines it with dry leaves or dead grass. She bears only one litter a year.

The mole babies come in March or April, after being carried in their mother's womb for thirty days. There are six to eight of them, and they are naked, completely blind, and helpless at birth. They are almost fully grown when they are two months old. Ten months later, in the following spring, they are ready to breed. Barring accidents, a garden mole will die of old age in its third year.

The male mole is not a "family man"; he may assist in building a nest during the courtship period, but even this is doubtful. Yet some co-operation from the male would really seem necessary. The mother must not only nurse her naked babies and keep them warm (for it is still cold in March and April), but she must often make extremely long trips in search of food for herself. Deprived of sustenance for a few hours, she would be on the verge of death by starvation.

The Star-nosed Mole, *Condylura,* of north-eastern North America, is the least molelike of all the American moles. It is an exceedingly strange-looking creature, and leads one to think, as the study of living things often does, that nature has left no experimental fields of development unexplored. For here is an animal with a naked fringe of twenty-two feelers, rose coloured and highly sensitive, symmetrically arranged in the shape of a disc on the tip of its nose.

This mole has a fat, scaly tail about three inches long, which is equal to its body length. Like other moles it has well-developed claws for digging. It wears a thick, jet-black coat of fur without lustre or sheen.

——FEELING ITS WAY. The star-nosed mole favours marshes and damp fields. It is as much at home in the water as in the soft earth, and can swim and dive like a muskrat. The feelers on its nose doubtless aid it in catching and identifying waterborne sounds and are used by the animal to feel its way about when submerged or underground and to detect the worms and insects on which it feeds. This species, like the rest of the moles, has practically lost the sense of sight; its sense of smell is weak.

THE MOLE THAT IS DIFFERENT

The star-nosed mole of north-western North America looks somewhat different from its run-of-the-tunnel relatives. This odd-seeming creature gets its name from a fringed disc on its nose tip. This peculiar nose helps the animal to locate worms and insects, its chief food. Sometimes, in the cold winter months, we are afforded a fleeting view of the star-nosed mole when it emerges briefly from the tunnels which it has hollowed out in the snow.

The star-nosed mole is the most sociable of the moles; it lives in small colonies from Labrador to Manitoba, and south to Georgia. Breeding time comes in the late autumn or early spring. During the mating season the animal's tail swells to at least twice its normal diameter. The first litter of young are born between the middle of February and May. There are from four to six babies in a family, and possibly a second litter is produced late in the summer. The baby moles are well-developed at birth, and at two months are out foraging for themselves.

The Hairy-tailed Mole, or Brewer's Mole, *Parascalops*, is quite different from other moles in that it inhabits upland wooded country. Most others favour low plains and meadowland. A little smaller than the eastern garden mole, this animal is black in colour and has a short, well-haired tail.

For no obvious reason, the hairy-tailed mole frequently ventures on the surface of the ground and becomes an easy prey for hawks, owls, and other flesh-eaters. Not only is this mole practically blind like other moles, but it does not detect airborne sounds any better. However, it is very sensitive to sound variations in its own element, the earth. It digs its tunnels nearer the surface than do moles of the common garden variety. The passages follow shady ridges and stone walls and are rarely marked by the usual unsightly molehills.

Hairy-tailed moles are scarce, and we know little about them. There is only one kind; its range is restricted to a strip in eastern North America from New Brunswick to southern Ontario and south in the Appalachian Mountains to North Carolina. A full-grown individual measures five inches from the nose to the tip of the one-inch tail. These animals are of little importance to man, either for good or for ill, since there are so few of them.

Flying Lemurs—Gliders of the Jungle

THE FLYING LEMUR, *Cynocephalus*, is a curious, exotic creature, found from the Malay Peninsula and Thailand to the Philippine Islands, Burma and Java. Normally about the size of a large squirrel, it looks much bigger when it spreads the furry membranes, or sails, attached to its long limbs, and takes to the air.

In spite of its name, the flying lemur does not actually fly—it glides or volplanes. Usually the animal launches itself on its aerial expeditions from the top of a tall tree and glides evenly and smoothly forward to another one. Even when there is no breeze it can travel as much as seventy yards with little loss in altitude. With a breeze it can cover a surprisingly greater distance. Moving in for a landing, it steers toward the desired tree and comes softly to rest, head up.

So thoroughly is the flying lemur adapted for soaring that it is at a disadvantage when it has to do other things. It cannot stand erect; it is practically helpless on the ground. It can climb, but only in a clumsy sort of way.

FLYING LEMURS

The flying lemur, about the size of a squirrel, is at home from the Philippines to Siam. It doesn't really fly—it glides, but can cover seventy yards or more in a single glide. Neither a squirrel nor a lemur, but a member of a family all its own, this odd-looking animal has a thin, furry flight membrane on either side of its body. The creature represents a transitional type—the first "birds" on earth were probably gliders like this one, before they acquired true wings. Seldom, if ever, does the flying lemur descend to the ground.

The colungo or caguan—that is what the natives call the flying lemur —is active only by night. In the daylight hours it sleeps. In a roosting position, it often hangs by its four feet, body down, like a sloth. Sometimes it may sleep wrapped around a branch; you may look directly at it and fail to see it, for it blends in perfectly with the bark of the tree.

The flying lemur is a slow breeder. As a rule it bears only one naked young each year, and it is not physically equipped to care for more than two. Like other animals that do not have a nest or a regular place to return to, the mother carries her baby wherever she goes. The baby clings to her breast in spreadeagle fashion as she journeys through the trees, feeding on fruits and leaves.

THE FLYING LEMUR'S STRANGE APPEARANCE

The flying lemur is extremely curious in appearance: it looks as though it were wearing a fur coat that reaches down to its toes. This is because on each side of its body the thin, furry flight membrane extends from the side of its neck to its thumb and between its fingers, down from its wrists to its ankles, and from the tip of its long outer toes to the end of its tail. When the animal is at rest, the membrane hangs in loose, voluminous folds. Covering its body is a coat of fine, soft fur that varies in colour from greyish to chestnut, irregularly broken with silvery-white spots and blotches.

As we might expect in an animal that is strictly a night-prowler, the flying lemur's eyes are large and prominent. But they are hazel in colour, which is rather surprising, as yellow pigment in the iris is usually for seeing in bright sunlight. The creature's four front teeth are unique among the mammals; each is compressed into a fine-toothed comb. Some say the animal uses them to brush its fur.

The flying lemur is not really one of the lemurs, although for many years scientists considered it a relative of those monkey-like creatures of Madagascar. Actually it is not closely linked to any other living mammal; it belongs in an order all its own, the Dermoptera ("skin wings"). There are only two living species.

The Bats

THE BATS we of the western world most often encounter have cunning pug faces and bright eyes. These little animals seem dreadful only to those who do not know their innocent habits. But there are other bats with enormous ears that fold like a concertina when not in use—bats with long, pointed faces—with flat faces—or with weird fleshy outgrowths on their muzzles. Some look fantastic, and a few can be described as hideous. No wonder superstitious people in all ages and lands have feared the bats and linked them with evil spirits.

There are bats with tails like mice; some have no tails at all. There are white bats, red bats, grey bats, piebald bats, black bats, and bats of many variations in colour. On their feet some species have suction discs which they use for clinging to smooth surfaces. Bats exist in such enormous variety that it is easier to say what they do not have than what they do have; there are no bats with actual trunks, quills, or shells.

The bats are built for flight. They are the only mammals that have real wings—wings not like the feathered pinions of a bird, but real wings none the less. Actually they are elastic membranes. Supported and spread by the bat's very long front limbs and fingers, these webs of skin extend all the way down to the animal's hind feet. (The bats' scientific name, order Chiroptera, means "winged arms", and in truth the wings are no more than modified forearms. The "thumb" is the only part of the hand that is the same as in other animals, and it bears a hooked claw.)

In most bats the membranes are also spread between the hind limbs and encase the tail, making it easier for the animal to float in the air. The bat's muscles and body structure are specially formed to support and operate the wings.

MYSTERY OF THE BATS' ORIGIN

These flying mammals have a very ancient lineage. In the dim ages of past geologic times, when the earth was tenanted by primitive land mammals such as the tiny four-toed horse, the bats were much as they are today. When they left the ground and took to the air, we cannot guess: there is a link missing between them and all other mammals. We know of no in-between types, no semi-fliers. Still, the flying lemurs and flying squirrels can travel a considerable distance in the air by gliding; they have no true wings, and are not capable of sustained flight. It may be that the first bats were gliders like these, and went on to develop into fliers.

WHERE WE FIND THE BATS

In the modern world we have found and named about two thousand different kinds of bats. Though certain kinds are restricted to certain regions, we encounter bats in all climates and countries from the Arctic to the Antarctic, except the Polar regions. Those in the colder parts of the world are active only during the summer months—for the winter season they either hibernate or migrate to a warm climate.

BATS AND THEIR FOOD

In general, there are two main kinds of bats—insect-eaters and fruit-eaters. The latter favour the tropics, where, incidentally, bats exist in the greatest numbers and tend to grow larger. The insect-eaters are smaller than the fruit-eaters, as a rule, but there are more of them. In size, bats vary from the enormous flying foxes, with a wing-spread of five feet, to tiny creatures no bigger than a humming-bird.

The diet of bats is not limited to fruit or insects. There are bats that eat meat, bats that go fishing, bats that draw the nectar from night-blooming flowers, and vampire bats that subsist on the blood they drain from the veins of birds and other animals. All, however, drink water regularly. They do not stop to lap it up like the cats and dogs, but skim the surface of the water like swallows and take their drinks in flight.

A NATURAL "RADAR" SYSTEM

Bats are supersensitive to sound waves. This capacity enables them to manoeuvre about in the dark as efficiently as a bird can in broad daylight. In fact, the bats already possessed a natural system of "radar" when man was still living in caves. In flight, a bat's mouth is open; it utters a continuous rhythm of sounds, pitched in a key too high for the human ear to recognize. These sound waves are thrown back to the bat by objects around it. By the use of its sensitive sound-perception ability, it can accurately determine its relation at all times to these objects, whether they be fixed or moving.

The author once met with a striking example of this ability when he disturbed a colony of several hundred bats in a small dark cave in the West Indies. All immediately took wing, swirling around in every direction, yet at no time were there any collisions. The orderliness of the seething, seemingly disorganized mass was incredible. Apparently each bat can recognize its own sounds, and not confuse them with those of its neighbours.

THE WEIRD NOSE LEAF

Certain bats have an outgrowth of skin and muscle on the muzzle and lips, generally referred to as a nose leaf. It varies in detail with different groups. Some entire families have only the slightest trace of a nose leaf, while on others it is long and lance-shaped, projecting straight up from the tip of the nose.

The use of the nose leaf is not yet well understood. Probably it acts as an antenna for the reception of air vibrations created by flying insects —it seems to be well developed in both fruit- and some insect-eating forms. Most bats also possess an extra spear-shaped flap growing in front of the ear opening. This flap, called a tragus, likewise helps the bat to detect sounds, we believe.

CREATURES OF THE NIGHT

Bats make no pretence of building any kind of nest. They usually have a regular place to roost, though—some dark or shady retreat such as a cave, a crevice in the rocks, a hollow tree, or just a shady tree, and they are not averse to taking advantage of human habitations as resting places. In tropical America there is a bat that actually makes its own shelter by scoring palm leaves, causing the sides to fold over and form a little tent. Bats sleep hanging head down, holding on with their feet.

Night is the time when bats are active. "Blind as a bat" is a meaningless phrase, however—contrary to popular belief, most bats can see perfectly well in bright light. The author has tried to catch one of the Kenya (African) species at noon as it clung to the bark of a great tree, but it scurried around the trunk in the sunlight, moving now slowly, now fast, and skilfully dodged every move made to capture it.

FAMILY LIFE AMONG THE BATS

Most bats are social. They live together in communities sometimes numbering as many as several hundred individuals. The peculiar thing about their social life is that normally the sexes do not intermingle in the communities. A colony of roosting bats is generally either all male or all female, although there are exceptions.

Most mammals go through some phase of courtship during the mating season, and among social animals a male will gather a harem of females. But not so with the bats. So far as we know, there is no segregation of mating pairs, no males collecting harems. There is free love among the bats—both sexes may have several mates.

Most bats mate only once a year. In tropical countries bats may mate in the early spring, but some pair off in August and September; these are the few that possibly breed twice a year. In temperate climates the mating season is in the autumn, but the embryo does not develop until the spring.

BAT BABIES AND MOTHERS

The bat mother usually produces one baby at a time; a few species have twins and one or two of the migrating bats bear up to four babies. The members of the female colony bear their young at approximately the same time, about 110 days after mating.

Baby bats, though tiny, naked, and blind, are well-formed, with well-developed wings. The baby opens its eyes for the first time when it is five to nine days old. From the very first it gets a feeling of flight;

it is carried about by its mother wherever she goes for the first thirteen days or so. When she roosts upside down, it clings to her breast and she supports it with her wings.

The female bat is an affectionate mother. The care and tenderness she shows her baby are as great as any we see among the other mammals. One of the classic stories about a mother bat's love for her young was recorded in *American Natural History*, 1826. It concerns a boy who had caught a baby bat and taken it home with him. Later that evening he was carrying the bat in his hand, on his way to a museum, when he passed the place he had captured the tiny animal. Its mother made her appearance and flew round and round him. Finally she alighted on his breast and both the mother and baby were taken to the museum, the young clinging to its parent. There are many stories like this on record.

At the age of two weeks, the baby bat is often too big a burden for the mother to carry with her. Now it is old enough to be left hanging by itself. But often this period of confinement is short. Within a few days the young bat is on the wing, learning all the tricks and aerial manoeuvres necessary to get its own living.

MOST BATS ARE USEFUL CREATURES

By and large, bats are useful creatures, and, for the most part, quite harmless. They do not habitually get into a person's hair, and they do not carry lice or bugs that might be troublesome to human beings. In the tropics some species wreak considerable havoc on fruit plantations, but most are insect-eaters and are of considerable economic importance in destroying mosquitoes and other insect pests.

Bats have a comparatively long life-expectancy. Large fruit bats live about ten or twelve years, with a top age of twenty years or so. Some of the common Little Brown Bats are known to have lived twelve years and may have a maximum of fifteen years or more. They have few natural enemies; owls and hawks in particular prey on them.

BATS IN OUR FOLKLORE

Bats loom large in our folklore. They have a strange likeness to human beings which even primitive man noticed. Some of the ancients believed the bats were once a sort of bird; dissatisfied with their lot, they flocked to sacred places to pray to be made like man. In answer to their petitions, the bats underwent a change in part: they gained the faces of men but their bodies remained birdlike. Ashamed to meet the birds in daylight, they are abroad only at night. But they still gather in the sacred places, temples, and churches by day, and pray that they may be changed back into birds.

Among the Finnish people we encounter the belief that during sleep the soul often takes the form of a bat—hence the disappearance of bats by day. Should a bat fly near anyone, it is held to be the spirit of someone dear. According to a similar tradition, at death the soul usually takes the form of a bird and flies to heaven, but if the death was violent the soul becomes a bat and remains on the earth for such time as God may determine. The ancient Mayas of Central America worshipped a bat god whom they considered a most powerful deity, and in Mexico there was a city by the name of Tzinacent Lan— "Bat City".

BATS AROUND THE WORLD

We find eight families of bats peculiar to the Old World, six to the New World; three families are common to both hemispheres. Of the Old World bats, two families are represented by a single species—the Short-tailed Bat, *Mystacina*, one of the only two land mammals native to New Zealand (the other is also a bat); and the Sucker-footed Bat, *Myzopoda*, of Madagascar. They are both the sole survivors of ancient lines of bats that have found safety on these island refuges, but they are now reaching the verge of extinction.

The Old World fruit bats and flying foxes are the first group which will claim our attention here. This family (the Pteropidae) lives in the warmer regions of the earth and includes some genuine curiosities like the long-tongued fruit bats (the Dawn Bat is one of the best known), which use their extendible tongues to lick out the pulpy juices of ripe fruit or the nectar of flowers, and even have a lower jaw shaped like a spoon. Another oddity is the Tube-nosed Bat—this strange denizen of the South Pacific region gets its name from its peculiar breathing apparatus, fleshy tubes extending beyond its mouth.

In their tropical and subtropical home, the fruit-eating bats are a distinct bother to plantation owners.

OLD WORLD FRUIT BATS AND FLYING FOXES

The Dog-faced or Rousette Bat, *Rousettus*, is a fruit and berry feeder. When the fruit on one of a grove of trees is ripe, the dog-faced bats are there in hundreds, whirling and squabbling over the choicest fruit. Some they eat on the tree, especially if the fruit is small, but they may carry large pieces away to convenient hang-ups, to be consumed at leisure. At the zoological gardens at Giza, near Cairo, large numbers of these bats feeding in the fig trees are a common night-time spectacle. Many are caught and eaten by barn owls.

In the daytime great numbers of these bats gather in the darkest corners of large caves, where they generally hang by both feet and spend much time in quarrelling among themselves; they are extremely noisy in the early morning. When the colony is disturbed, the screeching is suddenly hushed; then, with a rush of wings, the entire assemblage takes flight and streams out of the cave, whirling round and round outside until the disturbance is over.

The dog-faced bat is a large, short-faced creature, dull brownish or greyish brown in colour, with a wing-spread of twelve to eighteen inches, and a short tail. Like most other bats, it has a claw on its index finger to hook on to a branch or cave wall when alighting. There are numerous species of dog-faced bats spread throughout Africa and the Indo-Australian region, including the Solomon Islands, but none dwells on the mainland of Australia.

In Africa the natives add dog-faced bats to their black boiling pots to help out their meagre fare. Many of the natives have a particular cave that they visit regularly to keep their larder supplied with bats. However, they are reluctant to admit it, perhaps for reasons of a taboo.

The Flying Fox, *Pteropus*, is the biggest bat on earth. In flight, at close quarters, it presents an awe-inspiring appearance: it has a wing-spread of two to five feet and its body may be twelve inches long. The animal is dark grey or black, with a bright yellow or tawny mantle marking its shoulders. It possesses a face like a fox's—the muzzle is long and slender.

The flying foxes love company, often associating together in great multitudes during the day, in giant trees in the forest or overhanging a river. Colonies of several hundred individuals may sometimes occupy a single tree. They have a well-marked roost, where the branches are marred by constant use; the upper limbs of the same trees may be used year after year for generations, until they become quite bare of foliage.

——FLYING FOXES ARE INDIVIDUALISTS. At sundown all the bats leave the roost and wing their way in search of ripening fruits and berries. Such a raiding party may steal a considerable amount of fruit from a plantation.

If the home roost is on a small island offshore, in the evening the entire colony flies in mass to the mainland before dispersing in search

THE BIGGEST BAT ON EARTH

The flying fox, largest of the bats, may have a wing-spread of five feet; forbidding though the creature looks, it feeds mostly on fruit. The flying fox hunts by itself, and, although it roosts in colonies, each bat must have enough space so that it does not touch its neighbours.

of food. But, though many may fly together in one direction, they do not travel in regular flock formation. Except when roosting, these bats are highly individualistic and pay scant attention to each other as they pursue their separate inclinations.

Returning to roost, each tries to get the most favourable position. There is much commotion and quarrelling as newcomers fight for places already taken. It seems that the bats must be evenly spaced or have sufficient room so that they do not touch each other. The bickering continues into the day—it is a wonder that they get any sleep at all. Eventually most of them quieten down, hanging either by one or both feet with their heads bent down on their breasts and partly covered by the folded wings.

Flying foxes often supplement their fruit diet with small fish. The bats hover over the water and catch the fish in their feet. Then they make off to a nearby tree to devour the catch.

The social habits of these creatures vary with the seasons. From September to January both sexes flock together. When the mating season in February and March is over, the females leave the regular roost. The males stay on for a while, but they too soon seek other fields. In June the females, now heavy with young, return to the roost. There the single young is born in August or September—a few come earlier or later.

———WHERE WE FIND THEM. The flying fox is found in tropical Asia, eastern Australia, Madagascar, and the islands of the South Pacific, but not in China or Africa. Near the southern limits of their range, the flying foxes make regular seasonal migrations, moving north or south in large bodies. There are also local migrations governed by ripening fruits.

The flying fox has no tail. Like this animal in general appearance, except that it does possess a tail, is the Bare-backed Fruit Bat of the Celebes and Queensland. It is also known as the Spinal-winged Bat because the wing membranes are attached along the middle of its back (incidentally making the back look bare).

The Hammer-headed Bat, *Hypsignathus,* is Africa's largest bat; it has a head-and-body length of ten and one-half inches and a wing-spread of forty. The head, with its swollen face and pendulous upper lip, appears to be cut off short. Grotesque ruffles of skin surround the warty snout and the split lower lip.

——A POWERFUL VOICE. The hammer-heads dwell in large flocks in the forest. At sunset the whole colony takes off, not in a flash but as individuals. On entering the trees, the males start to utter resounding calls, each repeating the sound at intervals of half a second, until midnight. To produce this call, they have an enormous bony larynx, or sound box, that fills one-third of the body cavity and crowds the heart and lungs backwards and sideways.

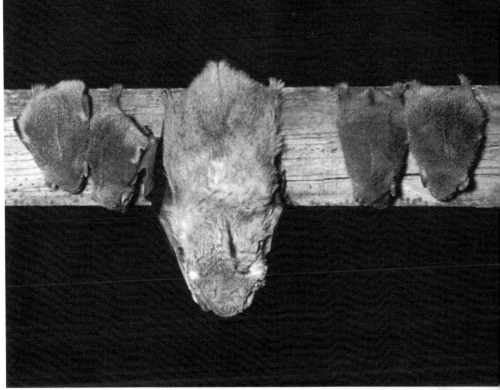

[1-15]

Almost all species of bats produce only one young at a time, but with the red bats multiple births are the rule. Twins are common, but on occasion there may even be quadruplets. *See page 127*

Some bats are solitary, but many are highly sociable, roosting in great squirming masses. *See page 101*

[1-15a]

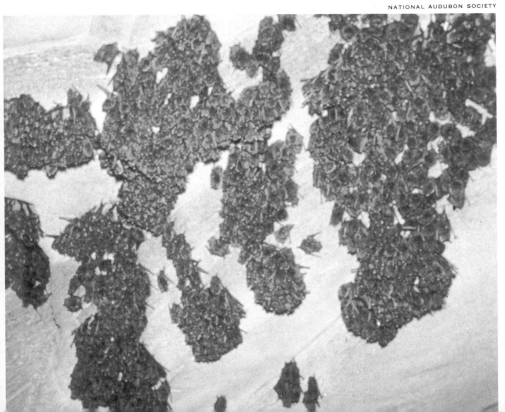

[1-16]

A long-eared bat. The spear-shaped growth ("tragus") in front of the ear opening is believed to be part of the bat's radar system. *See page 128*

NATIONAL AUDUBON SOCIETY

Although not the evil creature of the superstitious legends that surround it, the vampire bat is no myth. Luckily there are only three species of vampire, and these are not widely distributed.
See page 119

NATIONAL AUDUBON SOCIETY

[1-16a]

Exploring Nature with Your Child

TABLE OF CONTENTS

The following chapters are included as supplements to the successive volumes of this Encyclopaedia. This additional feature provides a Guide to Nature's Ways and Wonders for young people.

What Nature Exploring
Can Do for Your Child

CHILDREN are natural explorers. They have the true explorer's interest in their immediate surroundings as well as in faraway places, and they are eager to know why things are as they are. If you are a wise parent, you will look upon these qualities in your child as a sacred fire—always to be fed, allowed to die out never. An inquiring mind and zest for living are essential for a rich, interesting, and worthwhile life. Childhood is the time to nourish and strengthen these fine qualities.

Just as your child is a natural explorer, you are a natural guide. You help him find security and a sense of direction in the broad and bewildering world that men have made; so, too, you can guide him along Nature's ways—and give him a happy outlet and satisfaction for his natural curiosity and exuberance.

You can be a fellow-explorer, too, enriching your own life as well as your child's. As you look back on your own early years, you may recall the first time you noticed a bud opening into a flower, a bird building its nest, two colonies of ants battling against each other. You may remember that such intimate glimpses of Nature gave you a real thrill. Now, as a parent, you can find still more pleasure in learning about the ways of animals and the wonders of plants as you share your observing with your child. No need to go on a safari through Central Africa—delightful discoveries await you in your own garden, in city parks and suburban gardens, along woodland paths where you may hike, and by the side of lakes and streams or the ocean where you may spend a holiday.

There is no end to the wealth of experiences Nature holds in store for you and your child. In a park you can see squirrels burying nuts, providing for lean times in a season of plenty. You may observe a flock of wild ducks landing on a park lake for a rest during their long flight from summer to winter homes. Bees, butterflies, and ants have strange and wonderful ways that you and your child can watch with fascination for hours.

The diversion Nature offers you is more exciting than any invented by man, yet it is close at hand and costs you nothing. In many suburbs you may look out of the window in the morning and see a woodchuck nibbling its breakfast in a dewy field, or a rabbit scampering across the lawn, purposefully headed for the vegetable garden. You may watch spiders spinning silken traps, or see an exciting tug-of-war between a robin and an earthworm. In woodlands and meadows, in zoos and museums, there is even more for you to observe. No television, radio, or motion picture producer could invest in his productions the millions of years that Nature has spent in preparing these thrilling spectacles for you.

The Best Approach to Exploring Nature

What is the best method of exploring Nature? The answer depends on the individual child, for children vary in their approach to Nature's activities just as they differ in countless other ways. One child is full of curiosity about plant and animal life from the time he is an infant. Another is absorbed in fanciful ideas, while still another has a mechanical bent, remaining oblivious to natural wonders until you bring them to his attention.

And so exploring Nature is not always a simple matter: it is not just "knowing all the answers" or pointing out each tree or bird that you see. A background of information is invaluable, to be sure, but you must pass it on in such a way that you do not overwhelm the child's own modest discoveries. Awareness is essential, but it should not be carried to a point where your child considers you slightly eccentric. On the whole, the successful approach lies in encouraging his inquisitiveness and providing opportunities for him to satisfy his curiosity.

We Learn from Nature

Children with a practical turn of mind particularly enjoy hearing about ways in which man has put Nature's "inventions" to use. Outstanding among these devices is camouflage, applied so effectively by many birds and other animals for their own protection. This principle pointed the way for the change from army uniforms that made soldiers conspicuous targets to the deceptive, neutral earth and leaf tones used in battle nowadays.

Another debt we owe to Nature is the inspiration of bird flight, which has been carefully studied in advancing our own conquest of the air. Fish that swam in prehistoric seas, and many other creatures, have benefited from streamlining—another principle that we have put to use only recently. Wasps were adept at making paper from wood fibre centuries before human beings learned the technique. Our recent invention of radar is an old story to bats, which have a somewhat comparable system for getting their bearings as they fly sightless through treacherous passageways. These are just a few of the lessons that the practical-minded child—or any child—will enjoy having pointed out to him as he becomes acquainted with Nature's ways.

Overcoming Fear

Exploring Nature teaches children to overcome many baseless fears. Occasionally you find a boy or girl showing more timidity than enjoyment in encounters with animals. The reason for this may be difficult to trace, for a child sometimes has experiences of which his parents are not aware. I saw a case in point one day in a wooded stretch of a large city park where children where playing unsupervised. A big boy, hand outstretched, started to chase a little fellow, and was fairly hissing with menace:

"Spider! Spider!"

The smaller child was screaming in fright. My curiosity aroused as to the size of the creature inspiring his terror, I approached the older boy and asked if I might see the spider. He gave me a delighted smile and showed me what was in his hand: a small flower!

"I just wanted to scare him," he explained. "He didn't come close enough to see what I really had."

Meanwhile something remarkable had happened. The younger boy had not only stopped crying, but was coming slowly towards us. My interest in the "spider" had aroused his curiosity and was giving him courage to at least see what the "dangerous" creature looked like. It was strong evidence of the influence of older people on a youngster—to his advantage or detriment.

As we spend time with children out of doors, we become familiar with the fears they may have of little-known creatures. Once we realize that these fears exist, it is usually not difficult to set at rest any timidity that is really baseless. The remedy is simply to give the youngster an understanding of the dreaded animal.

"The Child is Father of the Man"

We contribute a great deal to a child's future happiness by giving him a sympathetic acquaintance with as much wild life as possible. The point is brought home to us when we meet an adult who is agitated by any number of groundless fears.

I remember, for example, a visit to our woodland cabin by a woman whose usual haunts were in New York. All day long she had been enjoying the trees and flowers, the river, and glimpses of bird life; but in the evening a screech owl's tremulous wailing whistle suddenly shattered the quiet. All our explanations about its being "only an owl" proved futile. Our visitor had been quite unnerved by the unearthly sound, and it was obvious she could hardly wait to return to what to her was the calming environment of the big city.

A few evenings later another visitor—this time a little boy of no more than five—heard the wail of the screech owl.

"What was that?" he asked.

We told him, hastily thinking of interesting facts that might dispel his fears. But we need not have bothered. As soon as he heard it was an owl, he said wistfully:

"I wish he would come close so I could hold him and pat him."

It is pleasant to think how rich life will be for this child, growing up with an acceptance of all the sounds and sights that have a rightful place in Nature's scheme. But he did not come by this attitude through chance. His parents have been giving him a knowledge and understanding of wild life since he was three. They have told him Nature stories and taught him Nature lore and hobbies that have widened his world and made it more enjoyable. All this will certainly contribute to a healthful serenity in later years.

You will find it easy—and delightful—to do the same for your child or children. You are building for the future when you instill in your child a true appreciation of Nature and outdoor activities. No one who has this heritage is likely to become a neurotic adult. His conception of the universe and our own earth and the life on it, including himself, is on too grand a scale to permit petty man-made problems to shatter his nerves.

Famous People as Nature Lovers

Many famous men and women began to take an interest in the world of Nature at an early age, and continued to study birds and beasts and flowers to the end of their lives. To some it was an absorbing hobby and the means of escaping for a time from the cares of everyday life, but others made it their life-work and gained fame, and sometimes fortune, from their study of living things.

Charles Darwin, who has been called the greatest of naturalists, was sent away to school at the age of eight. The school he went to was severely classical, and the headmaster is said to have been bitterly opposed to science; but in spite of this Darwin began to study the living world around him, often neglecting his Latin and Greek in order to do so. He collected flowers and insects, found out their names, and, which was much more important, he wondered why particular flowers were found in certain places and why insects behaved as they did. In this way he developed the scientific curiosity that was to be so useful to him later on.

Darwin left school at sixteen, and went to Edinburgh University to study medicine, but his love of Nature remained with him. He never became a doctor. The call of natural history was too strong, and in the end it claimed him. He lived to become a Fellow of the Royal Society, and the greatest naturalist this country has ever known.

Gilbert White was another who began to study natural history at an early age. He was born, the eldest of a family of eleven, in the village of Selborne, where he spent most of his life. When he was a boy he spent most of his time roaming over the downland near Selborne, making notes of the wild life that surrounded him. After taking a degree at Oxford he returned to Selborne as curate and spent the rest of his life studying Nature in between his parish duties, which were not heavy in so small a village. Gilbert White is best known as the author of *The Natural History of Selborne*, the most famous of all Nature books, but his greatest work was in laying the foundations of the science of ecology—the study of living things in their natural homes.

Sir Edwin Ray Lankester, although born a Londoner, also started his career as a naturalist when he was a boy. His father was a doctor with a deep interest in natural history, and from an early age Ray Lankester shared his father's passion for living things. He wrote his first scientific paper when he was only sixteen years old, and went on to become one of our greatest British zoologists.

In all countries, men and women have achieved eminence after evincing an early and continuing interest in the world around them, and particularly in Nature's ways. Their awareness of Nature has brought greater contentment and happiness into their own lives. Indeed, they have enriched the lives of all of us with the achievements of the inquiring mind that has been trained by close and habitual observation.

Why Nature is Important to Your Child

Modern schools have excellent programmes of Nature study; but even the best programmes cannot take the place of family participation in Nature interests. On the other hand, any child whose parents enjoy Nature with him finds this of real help with his schoolwork. He will readily discuss ideas that are presented to him at school when he knows his father and mother are interested.

Actually it is not always simple to keep up with the rapid strides made by children. It seemed I had barely stopped smiling over my three-year-old's comments, such as, "I know bees make honey, but I don't see *how* they get it into jars," when he was coming home from school asking, "What is the difference between rodents and other kinds of animals?" A year later he was likely to interrupt lunch with such posers as: "If dinosaurs were so big and powerful, why did they all die?" Suddenly we had arrived at questions that still puzzle many a scientist.

The important place that Nature has in the life of a young child has been sensitively analysed by Arnold and Beatrice Chandler Gesell. Here is what these eminent experts on child behaviour say:

"There is nothing new under the sun, but to childhood all is novelty. The most commonplace things teem with novelty.

"Children are in a stage of sense experience when this warm glow of contact through eye and ear and touch may be transmitted into the life of spirit; when light, shadow, sound, motion, and touch weave a tangle of lovely associations around commonplace experiences and build up a deep appreciation of life and things. Thus the truths of Nature become unconsciously associated with emotional response, which deepens and safeguards them. The child learns more through unconscious absorption than through didactic prescription, and in Nature study daily contact with the beauty, motive, and unceasing effort everywhere shown by plant and animal gives an impulse to individual character and sets standards of behaviour.

"The child who stands on tiptoe to peep cautiously into the new-found bird's nest, who feels the velvety softness of growing things beneath his feet as he hunts out the tiny wild flowers in the spring, who sows his own garden seed and waits to see the first young green push its way through the dark, moist soil is building up a reverence for life, a sense of kinship with it, which will uphold him in his later and deeper understanding of its meaning."

How to Understand the Birds

MOST children, as soon as they are old enough to take an interest in their surroundings, delight in birds. A bundle of feathers with bright eyes and a perky air of self-confidence is an appealing figure whether trilling on a summer day or seeking food in wintry gales. As the child matures, he looks more inquiringly at the graceful songster with which he has become familiar, and one day may startle you with the question:

"What makes a bird a bird?"

Taken off guard you might answer: "A bird has feathers and wings and is able to fly."

But there you stop in confusion. Some birds, such as the ostrich and penguin, do not fly! A fuller explanation will take this into account. Birds are warm-blooded, feathered, egg-laying animals that have backbone and wings, although the wings do not necessarily serve as flying aids. Naturally, you will have to expand this description to make it clear to a child—but it will fit the tiny, speedy hummingbird, the earth-bound ostrich, the majestic eagle, the comical puffin. It will fit the feathered creatures of woodlands, prairies, oceanic islands, high mountain slopes, lakes, deserts, jungles and barnyards. It will stand up under such a challenge as I had from a three-year-old:

"But, Mummy, you called the chicken a bird. It's a chicken!"

9

By strongly emphasizing feathers I finally persuaded her that even the stalwart barnyard fowl deserves to be ranked with the birds. Feathers are about the only feature which birds do not share with any other kind of animal.

Feathers for Clothes

Bird plumage is often so beautiful that we are likely to overlook its practical value. What clothes are to people, feathers are to birds: undergarments, overcoat and raincoat all in one.

Watch a chicken caught in a rainstorm and you will have a perfect illustration of the "raincoat". The chicken droops its wings and tail, making the best possible use of the feathers—for rain flows off them as it does from an oilskin coat. Examine one of the feathers and you will find it has three distinctive parts: the quill (or central stem); the barbs attached to the major part of the quill; and a soft fluff. This fluff, snuggling against the body at the base of the quill, plays the part of warm underclothing.

Why Protective Colouring is Important

Feathers often serve birds as camouflage. We quickly recognize this in many wild birds. The value of protective colouring in chickens is less obvious to us because we usually see them in a barnyard. Were a hen living in a state of nature, wandering in grassy fields with her chicks, her neutral colour would blend with her surroundings. It is the rooster who is decorative, having lovely iridescent tail feathers and, sometimes, colourful neck plumage.

Wild birds offer many convincing examples of the safety value of camouflage. The female golden oriole, for example, is a dull orange yellow while her mate is a brilliant combination of vivid orange, black, and white. The pheasant is another instance of the same kind of thing. The male is a gorgeous bird, highly coloured, with a glossy dark green head, scarlet wattles around the eyes, a white ring round his neck and plumage of varying shades of brown and greenish blue. The female is mottled blackish buff, without any vivid colouring, and is shorter-tailed.

In each case we see the same principle at work: the mother birds that must look after the eggs and babies do not attract notice. Meanwhile the arrestingly coloured males can remain at a suitable distance from the nest, distracting the attention of squirrels or other possible enemies.

You may notice an interesting phase of protective coloration in birds that are "moulting". When the males of certain species lose their bright feathers after the mating season, they develop new ones of sombre hues. By late summer the male scarlet garganey is the same dull yellow green as his mate; both male and female mandarin become sparrow-like in appearance; and the bright yellow body-feathers of the goldfinch have given way to others of dull yellow brown. So garbed, the male birds are fairly inconspicuous until the time comes again for them to be gaily attractive to the females.

New Feathers for Old

If late summer happens to be the time that your boy or girl starts to show a more than casual interest in birds, the subject of moulting makes the most dramatic theme to explore. Some species lose their worn and faded feathers in August, and by September have a completely new plumage. Among the exceptions to this schedule are waterfowl, which begin to moult in June. By September they have passed through two moults, during which they took on and discarded a dull plumage.

Unless there is a definite change in a bird's coloration during moulting, the process is not easy to observe, since the change is gradual. Starting with one certain feather—usually this is the innermost primary wing feather—it continues over the wings until all are replaced. The feathers of some kinds of birds develop all over the body at the same time, while on others the development comes in patches. Ducks, grebes, teals and other swimming birds which do not depend on flight as their only means of locomotion, moult all feathers at the ends of the wings (the primaries) within a very short time.

Feathers do not grow haphazardly over a bird's body, but are arranged in definite lines or patches (called "feather tracts") between

which there are bare areas. However, the overlapping of feathers
of the adjacent tracts keeps the skin completely covered in healthy
birds. You may see a chicken looking "half-naked" as the result
of arrested feather development. This never happens to wild birds
unless they are diseased.

Most birds moult only once a year, but the brilliantly coloured
males that have dull winter coats must change again to regain their
beauty in the spring. Hence such birds as the pied wagtail and the
goldfinch undergo a spring (prenuptial) as well as an autumn (post-
nuptial) moult. The spring moult is usually not complete, however;
the wing and tail feathers serve both plumages.

Some birds change appearance between winter and spring without
undergoing a second moult. They do so merely by "feather wear";
that is, the feather tips which have given the general tone to the winter
plumage wear away and expose the bright colours of the breeding
plumage. The robin is a notable example. His breast becomes redder
as autumn advances because the grey feather tips are wearing off.
In other birds yellow, brown, and grey most frequently edge the
feathers in winter plumage. As these colours disappear, black, brown,
or red is revealed.

Moulting consumes energy. While it is growing a new set of feathers,
a bird neither sings nor fights, staying in seclusion except when it
must seek food. It is for this reason, rather than because of an early
departure for southern climes, that you see few birds in late August
and early September. As soon as the birds have completed their
moulting they regain their vitality and are ready to migrate or to face
the rigours of a northern winter.

The Versatile Beak

The child who is always asking "Why?" will be fascinated by the
endless variety of bird beaks. In almost every case, beak formation
gives us the clue to a bird's eating habits, diet—and even its
surroundings. The duck, for example, has a wide, flat bill that equips
it for feeding on water insects and plants. After seizing food in
its beak, the duck holds the food until the water strains out of the
sievelike edges. Given the same conditions, the sharp, horny beak

of the hen would be quite useless. The hen's beak resembles a pick rather than a scoop, and it strikes efficiently into the soil for insects or seeds.

Another bird with a sharp, seed-eating beak is the sparrow. As for the woodpecker, its beak is virtually a chisel. You may spy one of these birds drilling for insects, or come upon the evidence where a woodpecker has left a series of holes in a tree trunk.

These are but a few examples of the close relationship between the style of a bird's beak and the kind of food that it eats. Children will get the point at once if you tell them the delightful Aesop fable of the stork and the fox. The stork, having been offered soup in a shallow dish by his host, a fox, gets his revenge by inviting the fox to dinner and serving it in a narrow-necked vessel down which its own long bill fits perfectly.

Getting food for the adult and feeding the young are the two basic uses of the beak. But it has other important functions. It is a tool for gathering nesting material and digging nesting sites, and it often serves as a weapon of attack or defence. It also enables many birds to do an effective job of preening and smoothing their plumage.

If the hen you watched during a storm could be observed after the rain stopped, you might see her using her beak to oil her feathers. There is an oil gland on her back, just at the base of the tail feathers. She presses the gland with her beak to force out oil; then she rubs the beak over the surface of her feathers and passes it through them. Now her "oilskin coat" is ready for the next downpour. A number of other birds, including waterfowl, use this same oiling method.

The parrot's curved bill is unique in construction and use, as it is a first-class climbing aid. The upper mandible, or beak, is movable, being connected to the bird's skull by a hinge. When the parrot climbs, it uses this mandible as a hook to support its body while its feet find a new resting place.

Feet are Versatile Too

Versatile as the beak is, the bird's feet are equally valuable tools. Wading birds, such as flamingos and herons, have extremely long toes

THE FLAMINGO—LONG AND LUGUBRIOUS

"Long" is the key word for the flamingo: long body, long bill, long neck, long legs, long toes. Its weird habits include: sleeping in its famous one-legged stance, eating with its head upside-down, and roosting on its foot-high cone-shaped nest.

which distribute their weight and keep them from sinking into soft mud. Short-tailed birds—the murres, for example—use the feet as rudders during flight. Diving birds, such as grebes, use their feet to propel them under water.

Whenever you see a bird scratching for food, you are noticing another use for its feet. Birds of prey, such as eagles and hawks, seize their victims in their long, powerful talons. Many birds use their feet to gather and place nesting material; with other birds, the feet are fighting weapons. The parrot uses a foot to grasp and bring food to its mouth, much as we use a hand. So we see that a bird's feet serve many purposes besides the most obvious one of supporting its body.

Sharp Eyes and Ears

Are the bright eyes of a bird as efficient as their alert and shining appearance leads you to believe? They really are. Birds are much more sharp-sighted than we are. Not only do birds have keen vision, but some of them are remarkably well adapted for seeing objects both far away and at close range. Thus a hawk flying so high that it would appear as a mere speck to us, may look down and see a rabbit or even a mouse on the ground! The hawk has two centres of vision, and as it swoops down from the heights, its vision shifts from one centre to the other so that its eyes are adjusted for short-range work when it seizes its prey.

Yet most birds, despite their sharp eyes, do not have bifocal vision like the hawk. One consequence is that they do not detect telephone and telegraph wires, and many birds are injured or killed every year by collision with such obstacles.

Among birds there is quite a bit of variety in the colour of the iris; it may be brown, grey, blue, yellow, white, pink, purple, green, and even red. The red-eyed vireo takes the first part of its name from this striking feature. The hen, which is ideal for bird study, has a yellow iris. It is equipped with an eyelid that shuts out vision, coming up from the bottom of the eye, however, rather than down from the top. It also has another kind of eyelid —a film that moves across the eye from the inside corner to the outer side.

You may escape questioning about a bird's hearing ability because their ears are fairly well hidden. Then suddenly this very fact may be the basis for a query from your young observer:

"How can that bird hear? I don't see any ears!"

Except for the owls, which have noticeable "ear tufts", the ear of a bird is no more than a hole, rather well covered with feathers, on the side of its head. Yet a bird's hearing is just as remarkable as its sight —perhaps even more remarkable. Walking in a field or forest you may notice how the snapping of a small twig will startle and put to flight a bird that is a considerable distance away. And when you see a robin cocking its head and realize it is listening for an earthworm under the surface of the ground, you develop a well-deserved respect for birds' hearing.

How Birds Fly

"How *do* birds fly?" is a question that most children ask at some time. The child may accompany his query with a leap into the air, arms outstretched, and a faint hope that he too can "take off".

BIRDS ARE BUILT FOR FLIGHT

It helps your inquisitive child to understand the mechanics of flight if you point out that the bird's streamlined form is of great advantage in flying. Besides this, it has an extremely light structure. Its bones and the shafts of its feathers are hollow and, as is easily seen, the size of its wing is greater in proportion to its body than an arm is to the human body.

You can then go on to compare the child's framework to the bone-and-feather structure of the bird, which has a bone corresponding to his upper arm and another to the bone between his elbow and wrist. Let the child extend his thumb upward, hold his first and second fingers in a horizontal position, and fold the other two into his palm—somewhat as he would do in making a pretend-gun out of his hand. This will give him a rough comparison with the structure of a bird's wing.

The bird has a winglet corresponding to the child's thumb, and a second and third digit similar to his extended fingers. These are sometimes extended upright, but may also be held horizontally. While the child's arm, hand, and fingers are covered only with skin, the bird has flight feathers also—one sheath on the "forearm", and another series on the "hand". The number of feathers varies in different birds.

FLIGHT TECHNIQUES

There are four types of bird flight: flapping, gliding, static soaring, and dynamic soaring. In flapping flight the "arm" wings help to lift most large wings into the air, while the "hand" wings produce propulsion through the air. Speed or forward motion is gained with each downward stroke of the wings; lift is obtained on up-and-down strokes. In this up-and-down motion the wing tips move through a much greater arc than the wrists would. (In aircraft flight lift and speed are produced by the propeller *and* the wings.) In small birds, such as the finch, the whole wing flaps as a unit, producing speed and lift at the same time. During the upstroke, the wing is folded.

When a bird glides, it loses altitude to keep its forward-pushing motion. In static soaring, the bird takes advantage of up-air currents which offset the loss of altitude suffered during its gliding flight. For dynamic soaring a bird such as the albatross will use the force of the wind. Wind force increases with altitude hence the bird, after descending most of the way, levels off with the slowing down of the wind near the surface of the water, and then ascends again, once more making use of the air currents.

Birds use their wings differently, depending on the kind of flight, such as horizontal, soaring, descending, gliding, hovering, taking off, and climbing.

Various types of birds necessarily have wings of different shapes and proportions, and each employs each wing in the distinctive manner appropriate to it.

An important feature of the bird's flying mechanism is a sinew with elastic qualities. On the downward thrust of the wing, the sinew holds the feathers in a tight overlapping position. When the wing comes up, the tension of the sinew relaxes and the feathers part and rotate. This arrangement allows air to flow between them as an aid in flight.

It gives us pleasure to understand how birds fly, but all the analysis in the world cannot dim the initial thrill of seeing birds in flight.

The Mystery of Migration

There is no greater mystery in the whole complicated story of bird behaviour than bird migration, for we do not know why they do it, nor how they manage to find their way, sometimes across thousands of miles of land and sea, to their breeding quarters, and then find their way back again the following year. How does the English swallow travel more than five thousand miles to South Africa in the autumn, returning in the spring, not merely to England, but to the locality from which it set out? How does it know when it is time to go, and when to return? How does it navigate for thousands of miles, without a compass, and know when it has reached its destination? These are just some of the questions posed by the migration of birds.

WHERE DO BIRDS GO?

There are many birds that do not migrate at all, for you can see them all the year round in the same locality. Such birds are the robin, the blackbird and the wren. We call these birds residents, or sedentary species, and they are sometimes, though not always, rather unsocial, like the robin that marks out its own territory and will allow no other robin save its mate to enter it. Even these sedentary birds may not always stay in one set locality, however. Greenfinches, at the approach of winter, may desert high ground for low-lying fields. We might regard this sort of thing as the beginning of migration —the kind of behaviour from which the habit of migration arose long ago.

Among British residents we may number the partridge, grouse, wren, house sparrow, barn owl, woodpecker (all three species) and many others.

In Britain it is customary for migrant birds to fly south in the autumn, towards a warmer climate, and to return in the spring to build their nests and rear their young. But we also have species that come to us from farther north in the autumn, leaving us in the spring and returning to Arctic or near-Arctic regions to breed. We can therefore distinguish between *summer migrants* that breed in these islands, and *winter migrants* that come to us from colder latitudes, to which they return when the weather improves.

Some birds travel astounding distances in the course of migration. We have already mentioned the swallow, which gets as far as South Africa, and other birds which regularly cross the Equator are the swift, the sedge warbler, the garden warbler, the marsh warbler, the willow warbler, the house martin, the sand martin, the nightjar, the corncrake, the cuckoo and the red-backed shrike. Some do not go quite as far: the nightingale, the wood warbler, the redstart and the wryneck, for instance, visit North Africa, but do not cross the Equator.

Other birds migrate for shorter distances. Sometimes the summer breeding quarters partially overlap the winter quarters. If you happened to live about half-way between the northern summer limits and the southern winter limits of one of these species, you would not notice that it was a migrant, for it would be in evidence all the year round. The actual birds you saw in the summer, however, would not be the same birds as the ones you saw in the winter, though to you they would look the same. Birds that behave like this are sometimes called *partial migrants*. The starling might be taken as an example.

HOW DO BIRDS FIND THEIR WAY?

Everyone who has heard of bird migration must have asked this question at some time or another, probably without getting a very satisfactory answer. We simply do not know how the migrants manage to navigate for such vast distances with such precision. There are really two sides to the problem: first orientation, and then navigation. When birds set out on their long journey, they must first orient themselves correctly: if their destination is South Africa, it would not do for them to head for the North Pole. Birds must have some kind of sense that tells them when they are headed right, just as some people can always tell which direction is north. There is actually some evidence that birds can both tell their position and set their course by means of the sun and stars, just as a sailor finds his way about the globe. This does not mean that they consciously "take a shot" of the sun to get their bearings, of course, but the instinct may be there just the same.

Whatever sense it is that guides birds in migration, it is not memory of having done the course before. The young cuckoo, deserted by its parents before it was even hatched, turns up in South Africa on time, its parents having made the journey a month or more ahead of it.

SKY LANES OF THE BIRDS

Some birds migrate regularly in company. Geese often travel in skein after skein, thousands of birds travelling together, and on occasion resting together at some suitable stopping place on the way. They may have regular migration tracks, like shipping routes or the sky lanes of airlines. Goldfinches, too, often travel in great convoys. Other birds journey alone, or in small family parties, like the swallows, meadow pipits and redstarts. When crossing the ocean they may take a short rest on a ship that happens to be in their course, but they usually do not stop for long.

Birds vary in the time of day they choose for their migratory flights. Some prefer to go by day, others by night. Amongst those that travel by day are geese, crows and swallows, while warblers, thrushes and woodcock are night fliers. Ducks go any old time.

HOW FAST DO BIRDS FLY?

There used to be fantastic stories about the speed of birds when flying, especially when migrating, but most of these have been shown to be false. A hundred miles an hour has been reached by the swift, an exceedingly fast bird, but this is quite exceptional. Migrating birds have a long way to go, and it would not do for them to use up all their energy in one burst of speed. Their usual speed on migratory flight is between twenty and fifty miles an hour. Those that fly very long distances pause from time to time for a rest.

THE SWALLOW—MIGRATOR EXTRAORDINARY

Every year the swallow leaves this country and flies more than five thousand miles, its destination being South Africa. There it stays during the English winter, and in the spring it comes back again. How it finds the way we do not know.

HOW TO KEEP A BIRD CALENDAR

If you live in a region where the four seasons are clearly defined by sharp weather contrasts, the study of bird migrations will provide you with an especially enjoyable hobby. By keeping a bird calendar you can note the comings, the goings, and the passings through of different species. Your calendar can be quite simple: a large ruled sheet of paper, divided into four columns. Head the first column "Date", the second "Bird's Name", the third "Where Seen", the fourth "Time of Day". You may simply fill in information about birds that come near your home, but the record becomes far more lively when you widen the range of observation by means of bird walks.

Some children enjoy such a project as an individual enterprise. Others are more stimulated if the calendar is a family affair with scope for friendly rivalry. Who will have the fun of recording the first nightingale of spring? Who will see a cuckoo this year? Who will trace a house martin by its lilting melody or look for a plover near its nest? Interest becomes keener when you keep calendars year after year, trying to better the record of observation with each new calendar.

How to Be a Good Neighbour to the Birds

There are a number of ways to bring wild birds close to your home where you may enjoy them and study them. One of the most effective overtures of friendship is to provide a birdbath. Songbirds as a rule seem to be attracted by water. Some of them even relish taking a bath when it is raining; but during hot dry spells when many natural sources of water dry up, your birdbath will serve a really essential purpose.

There are also times when birds have trouble finding drinking water. The simplest way to provide a bath and drinking fountain is to set a shallow pan filled with water on the ground, on a post, or on a ledge. In placing the pan, keep in mind the danger from cats. These enemies must not have any nearby hiding place from which to launch a surprise attack against the birds. A birdbath of concrete comes near to being ideal because its dull surface blends well with the browns, greens, and greys that surround it, and its rough surface makes perching easy.

FEEDING THE BIRDS IN WINTERTIME

You can also attract birds by building houses and shelters for them. But probably the greatest service you can render is to furnish winter food. Though completely self-reliant in warm weather, the birds that remain in the north throughout the year are often desperate for food during the winter months. Birds have an exceptionally high body temperature, and so long as they have sufficient food to keep this temperature normal they do not suffer from the cold. But if a scarcity of food results in a lowering of the body temperature, the birds suffer severely and may even freeze to death.

You can provide food for them in a number of ways. If you have a garden, simply trample down the snow at some suitable spot and sprinkle crumbs and seeds. Or else you may tie pieces of suet to trees or posts. A feeding-tray fastened to a window makes a good, safe feeding station, and also gives you a wonderful opportunity to watch birds at close quarters. You can even photograph them without much trouble. Cut a circular hole at the bottom of a board that fits into the window frame where your feeding-tray is placed. When you wish to take pictures you can raise the window, insert the board barrier, and direct your camera through the hole. Birds will partake of your food offering without the least alarm as they let themselves be photographed.

One other excellent type of feeding station is a *covered* platform attached to a post. The covering keeps the food dry and the elevation protects the birds while they are eating. There are many other efficient types of bird feeders that you can buy or make and place on porch or window sill, or around the garden.

WHAT BIRDS FEED ON

Different birds have different preferences in the way of food. Many insect-eating birds, such as redwings and woodpeckers, will eat suet when insects are not available. Seed-eating birds are usually not tempted by fat, but they will eat stale bread, biscuits and cake broken into crumbs, as well as sunflower seeds. You can buy packets of bird seed specially for feeding wild birds. An excellent food for birds can be made by frying small lumps of bread in suet, bacon fat or fat cut off the joint; in winter, birds will congregate in dozens and fight over a dish of this, and the contents of even the largest frying pan are soon gone.

If you can get hold of a coconut, cut it in half and hang the halves in a tree, or from the bird-table. Blue tits are particularly fond of coconut, and will perform acrobatics on the swinging half-nuts as they dig out the contents.

THE GROUSE—SPORTSMAN'S FAVOURITE

These handsome game birds are great favourites with hunters. Grouse are hardy creatures, accustomed to living through the rigours of a severe winter. When their usual insect diet is not available, they make do with twigs and buds.

Let me give one word of warning. If you have an active cat you must forgo the pleasure of feeding birds in the garden. It is not fair to tempt birds into danger with morsels of food.

Birds as Songsters

All birds have voices and many are very beautiful indeed. We can distinguish between birds that sing and birds that merely call, and again between birds whose call is melodious and those in which it is harsh and unmusical. The distinction is a little artificial, for birds that sing also call; in fact, those with a good vocabulary may have up to twenty different calls, each of which seems to mean something to the birds, and to birds that hear them.

Amongst song birds we find the blackbird, song thrush, missel thrush, skylark, robin, wren, meadow pipit, and many others. Equally familiar are those birds which call on a musical note, though they do not indulge in sustained song; among them are the lapwing, cuckoo, bullfinch, blue-tit and sandpiper. Amongst birds which have an unmusical call are the raven, carrion crow, rook, magpie, house sparrow and pheasant.

We do not know what the voices of the first birds were like, though we know something of their appearance from fossilized remains. They evolved from reptiles about a hundred and fifty million years ago, and had scaly bodies, traces of which can still be seen in the scales on the feet of modern birds. We can safely assume that they knew nothing of song, though it is possible that they were able to grunt or squeak when they were angry or afraid. When they left the ground and took to perching in trees, out of the way of enemies, they had more time and freedom in which to develop the habit of song, and it may well have been this that led some of them to become songsters.

BIRDS THAT HOP AND BIRDS THAT WALK

There are two kinds of birds: those that hop with both feet together and those that walk and run as we do. The birds that hop are accustomed to feeding in trees as well as nesting there. They hop from twig to twig, looking for berries or insects, and they have got out of the habit of walking. Birds that nest in trees but feed on the ground as well as birds that both nest and feed on the ground, have retained the walking habit.

It is clear that birds that both nest and feed in trees lead the safest lives, for they need seldom use the ground with all its dangers from cats, stoats and other enemies. It is a significant fact that nearly all our song birds, as well as those with musical calls, hop instead of walking. They live in trees. Birds that spend a lot of time on the ground in general do not have such musical voices as the tree-livers. Of course, there are exceptions to this: the skylark, for instance, one of our most beautiful songsters, nests and feeds on the ground.

WHY DO BIRDS SING?

Birds sing for many reasons, of which perhaps two are particularly important. In the spring, when it is mating time, the male birds in particular sing to attract a partner. When birds are courting it is usually the male who puts on the show, displaying his plumage to its best advantage and bursting into a riot of melody to show the female bird what a fine fellow he is. It is hardly surprising, therefore, that spring is the best time for hearing bird song, nor is it so strange that often it is the male bird who is a songster, while the female is restricted to calling.

THE GOLDFINCH—ECSTATIC SONGSTER
Like their famous relatives the canaries, goldfinches are inspired singers. They sing while perching and sometimes bound into the air with an ecstatic outburst of twittering notes. The goldfinch flies in graceful curves that are a pleasure to watch.

The other important reason why birds sing is to mark out their territory. Many birds have an area of ground that they regard as their own, and will suffer no intruders. Robins are particularly zealous in guarding their territories from other robins, and their song when they are doing so is a warning to others to keep out. If a robin should wander into another's territory he is soon chased out again, and then the victor will perch in a prominent place and sing a song of victory.

OTHER BIRD SOUNDS

Besides its song, a bird can usually produce a number of other sounds for various purposes. When birds are young they can often make a peeping sound that lets their parents know where they are, and similarly the mother may call to her young. Many birds have calls that mean danger, and there may be different calls to indicate what is frightening them. The yellow-breasted chat has four calls, each indicating different degrees of alarm.

Mothers may warn their young of danger by a particular call. The golden-naped woodpecker has a warning call which causes her young to come home immediately, while when the ptarmigan utters her warning the chicks scatter at once into the surrounding herbage.

IDENTIFYING BIRDS BY THEIR SONG

If you use your eyes and ears when you are out you should soon be able to recognize some birds from their songs. Listen for a distinctive song or call, and then look to see what bird is making it. If you do not recognize the bird at sight you can look it up in a book when you get home. Next time you hear that song, try to remember what the bird looked like. You will soon become proficient, and you will find that it adds a lot of pleasure to a country walk.

It sometimes helps if you can make up words to fit the song. A thrush, for instance, seems to be saying "cup-of-tea, cup-of-tea", while a yellow hammer says "a-little-bit-of-bread-and-*no*-cheese". A chaffinch quite clearly says "pink-pink".

The easiest birds to recognize from their calls are those that repeat their own names. Everyone knows the sound of a cuckoo, and the chiff-chaff is another bird that announces himself with equal clarity.

Do not be put off if your friends disagree with you about what birds "say". It may sound different to them.

How to Make Birds Feel at Home

One of the most satisfying outlets for the energies of a young carpenter is building a bird house. As he uses his tools he gets a practical grasp of the essentials of construction work. Later on, if he keeps an eye on the house after it is set up, he will learn a great deal about the habits of birds and their likes and dislikes. As he sees them in and about "his" house, he will experience a feeling of pride and protective tenderness.

But remember that birds are often very "choosy", inspecting and rejecting, or simply ignoring, an ideal-looking residence designed for them and nesting near by in a hollow stump, or tree.

Baby Birds

THE CHICKEN AND THE EGG

The best-known bird's egg by far is that of the chicken. It is such a common sight on grocery shelf and breakfast table that it really requires an effort of imagination on a child's part to think of the egg in connection with bird life.

Yet if, in this day of incubators, children could watch a hen with her brood, they would soon realize she is one of the best of bird mothers. When she takes her chicks into tall grass she clucks constantly so that they will not stray away from her. Finding a bit of food, she calls them quickly and they understand just what she means. Should a hawk appear overhead, she gives a warning cry which sends the chicks scurrying for cover. If a rat or other enemy threatens her brood, she will fight to the limit of her strength to protect the chicks.

A newly hatched chick wears an odd little "bump" on the tip of its upper mandible, or beak. This is the "egg tooth" that the baby used as a pick to break its way through the eggshell. After the egg tooth has served its purpose the chick has no further use for it and it soon disappears.

HOW MANY EGGS ARE LAID?

There is an almost endless variety in birds' eggs. There are big eggs and little eggs; white, coloured, and spotted eggs; eggs that differ in shape and length of time required for incubation. And so you need considerable information to answer the simple question: "How many eggs does a bird lay?"

We have no unconditional reply to this question. Each species has a *usual* number that makes up a full set; but differences will still crop up. Northern thrushes, for example, normally lay four eggs, while tropical thrushes lay only two or three. If a nest is robbed, the bird will often lay additional eggs to replace the stolen ones. There is an historic case of a brown woodpecker—known as the flicker—laying seventy-one eggs in seventy-three days!

THE AMAZING HUMMING-BIRD

The smallest of all birds, with the tiniest of eggs, the humming-bird has other claims to fame. Besides flying backward or remaining stationary in mid-air, it can move its wings so rapidly that they become invisible. This incredibly rapid motion produces the sound that gives the "hummer" its name.

Fantastic as this may sound, it illustrates the fact that constant nest-robbing has virtually turned domestic fowls into egg-laying machines. A domestic hen may lay more than two hundred eggs a season if they are promptly taken away, thus assuring "continuous performance". On the other hand, if the eggs are left in the nest to be incubated, her production will stop after fifteen or twenty eggs.

The best you can do, then, in giving actual numbers of eggs that different birds have in a clutch, is to say that in a full set of eggs there may be as many as twenty or as few as one.

THE SIZE OF EGGS

"Which bird lays the biggest eggs?" and "Which lays the smallest?" are welcome questions because we have direct and definite answers to them. The ostrich, largest of birds, lays the largest eggs; the humming-bird, smallest of birds, lays the smallest eggs.

However, it does not always follow that the larger bird lays the larger egg. A bird whose chicks come forth in a well-developed state, lays relatively larger eggs than a bird whose chicks are less well developed.

Among the well-developed babies are those of our friend the chicken, the grouse, and the spotted sandpiper. When they hatch they are already covered with a soft down. Their eyes open immediately and in no time at all they can toddle about and follow their mother. Before long they learn to pick up and eat their own food. We term this kind of bird "precocial", a word related to "precocious". Birds that hatch in a more helpless state are naked or at best have a scant covering of down. They are blind at first and are dependent on their parents for at least a week—usually much longer. Such birds are known as "altricial", from the Latin word for "nourishers".

"BABY SITTERS"

The length of time needed for incubation varies with different species. The English sparrow takes twelve or thirteen days; the robin, thirteen or fourteen days; the hen-harrier, about four weeks. In some families the duty of sitting on the eggs is shared by both parents; in others, it falls entirely to the lot of the mother. There is one curious family in which the eggs, once they have been laid by the female, become the sole responsibility of the male. He incubates the eggs unaided, though the mother stays near by and shows continued

interest in her family. These birds are the phalaropes, Arctic birds
sometimes seen in northern Scotland.

BRINGING UP BABY

Helpless baby birds require an extraordinary amount of care, and
perhaps because it helps to build in themselves a sense of the security
of parental care and affection, children greatly enjoy hearing about
the devoted family life of birds. How proud the mother hen is
of her chicks as she struts about the barnyard, clucking loudly to
call attention to her brood! In the wilds, where danger constantly
threatens, the mother bird's behaviour may be quite the opposite
—she does everything possible to make her brood inconspicuous.
A grouse, sensing an intruder, will go to the extreme of chirping
pitifully while thrashing along the ground as if hurt. This serves
two purposes. Her cry warns the young to remain quiet or escape
from the danger, and her movements divert attention from her little
family.

HOW BIRD BABIES ARE FED

Bird babies have enormous appetites. Until they are able to take
care of themselves, their parents must find and bring them food.
The fledgelings usually feed on insects, even though many of them
will grow up to be seed-eaters. In species where the young are
most helpless—the mourning dove, for example—the parent first
swallows the food and then feeds it to them in partly digested form.
That is why one of these birds, unlike so many other bird parents, is
never seen flying back to the nest with food in its bill.

Children occasionally have the good fortune to watch baby birds
being fed. More often the children see pictures of the birds at feeding
time, and they may notice that feeding techniques vary with
different birds. The most common method is for the parent to
push its bill down the baby's throat—a method that prevents any
live insect from escaping. With pelicans and certain other species
that regurgitate food, the process is reversed. The baby puts its
head in its mother's throat pouch or takes food from her bill.
The babies' need for water is satisfied by the moisture in their
solid food.

Parents often continue feeding the young after they have left the nest; but at this point the feeding methods are no longer so painstaking. The swallows are particularly interesting to observe at this stage of development. While in the nest, the young bird has food carefully placed down its throat. But once the fledgeling is able to hop away from the nest, it must be on the alert with bill opened upward, for the parents merely drop food to it without pausing in their flight. When the young swallows start to fly, this catch-as-catch-can feeding continues while the parents and the young birds as well are in full flight.

Proper manners, as taught to our children, are out of place as far as baby birds are concerned. Usually the aggressive one that stretches its neck farthest and cries the loudest is the one that is fed—until another member of the family becomes more "grabby". However, the parent, with a kind of rough justice, usually looks into the youngster's mouth after each feeding; if a morsel has not been swallowed instantly, the older bird snatches it back and turns its attention to another baby.

GETTING READY TO LEAVE THE NEST

Some babies—those of chickens, for example—are covered with down and able to run about when newly hatched. The parents may keep them under their wings, "brooding" them over a period of five or six weeks. Other kinds of birds also "brood" while the babies are in the nest, but never after they have started to fly. Brooding protects the young ones from the cold—and from excessive heat as well, as it prevents their being overheated in a nest unprotected from the sun.

As the baby birds develop feathers, their responsibilities grow. They preen their feathers, and begin to exercise, concentrating on stretching their wings. Often they practise "taking off" before leaving the safety of the nest.

Though birds fly by instinct, the first flight generally requires considerable parental coaxing. It may be no more than a flutter to a nearby limb or it may be, as in the case of swallows, a sustained and graceful performance. Song sparrows and others are ready to try their wings only a week after hatching, while the wandering albatross has to be forced out by its parents to make room for a new brood—nearly a year later. But whatever the amount of time involved, the youngsters have flourished on the solicitous care of their parents, and are now ready to face life on their own.